Scholastic

LITERACY PLACE

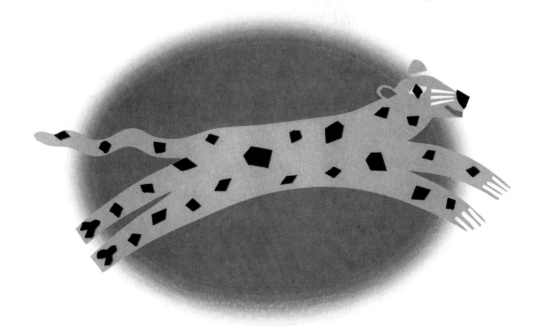

Copyright acknowledgments and credits appear at the end of this book. These pages constitute an extension of this copyright page.

Copyright © 1996 by Scholastic Inc.   All rights reserved.   Printed in the U.S.A.
ISBN 0-590-59265-3

3 4 5 6 7 8 9 10   24   02 01 00 99 98 97

The Funny Side

UNIT
5

NATURE GUIDES

UNIT 6

IT TAKES A LEADER

The Funny Side

JUMPSTART
BY ROBB ARMSTRONG

Step into
a Cartoonist's Studio

Sometimes humor is the best way to communicate.

A Laugh a Day

Our sense of humor lets us find funny stories in everyday events.

"All your wishes shall be
granted," cried the fairy,
"Ziz Ziz Boom, Tic Tac Ta,
This empty can shall be a car."

What's So Funny?

Surprise and exaggeration can make things seem funny.

Oodles of Noodles

Funny People

People use humor to entertain each other.

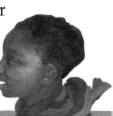
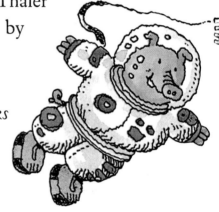

Trade Books

The following books accompany *The Funny Side* SourceBook.

Chocolate-Covered Ants

by Stephen Manes

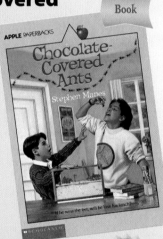

The Cybil War

by Betsy Byars

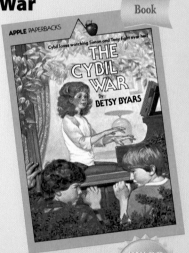

James and the Giant Peach

by Roald Dahl
illustrated by
Nancy Ekholm
Burkert

The Stinky Cheese Man

by Jon Scieszka
illustrated by
Lane Smith

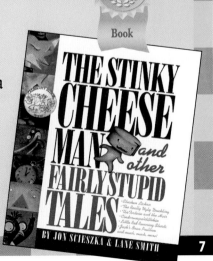

Our sense of humor lets us find funny stories in everyday events.

A Laugh a Day

Meet Fudge, who gets the family into one sticky situation after another. Then find out why laughing is good for you.

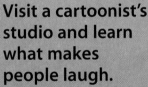

Visit a cartoonist's studio and learn what makes people laugh.

Discover what space aliens think about a popular pet.

WORKSHOP 1

Choose a favorite fairy tale and create your own fractured fairy tale.

"All your wishes shall be granted," cried the fairy. "Ziz Ziz Boom, Tic Tac Ta, This empty can shall be a car."

AWARD
WINNING

Book

from
TALES OF
A FOURTH GRADE
NOTHING

Mr. and Mrs. JUICY-O

by
JUDY BLUME

illustrated by
LIZ CALLEN

One night my father came home from the office all excited. He told us Mr. and Mrs. Yarby were coming to New York. He's the president of the Juicy-O company. He lives in Chicago. I wondered if he'd bring my father another crate of Juicy-O. If he did I'd probably be drinking it for the rest of my life. Just thinking about it was enough to make my stomach hurt.

My father said he invited Mr. and Mrs. Yarby to stay with us. My mother wanted to know why they couldn't stay at a hotel like most people who come to New York. My father said they could. But he didn't want them to. He thought they'd be more comfortable staying with us. My mother said that was about the silliest thing she'd ever heard.

But she fixed up Fudge's bedroom for our guests. She put fancy sheets and a brand-new blanket on the hide-a-bed. That's a sofa that opens up into a bed at night. It's in Fudge's room because that used to be our den. Before he was born we watched TV in there. And lots of times Grandma slept over on the hide-a-bed. Now we watch TV right in the living room. And Grandma doesn't sleep over very often.

My mother moved Fudge's crib into my room. He's going to get a regular bed when he's three, my mother says. There are a lot of reasons I don't like to sleep in the same room as Fudge. I found that out two months ago when my bedroom was being painted. I had to sleep in Fudge's room for three nights because the paint smell made me cough. For one thing, he talks in his sleep. And if a person didn't know better, a person could get scared. Another thing is that slurping noise he makes. It's true that I like to hear it when I'm awake, but when I'm trying to fall asleep I like things very quiet.

When I complained about having to sleep with Fudge my mother said, "It's just for two nights, Peter."

"I'll sleep in the living room," I suggested. "On the sofa . . . or even a chair."

"No," my mother said. "You will sleep in your bedroom. In your own bed!"

There was no point in arguing. Mom wasn't going to change her mind.

She spent the day in the kitchen. She really cooked up a storm. She used so many pots and pans Fudge didn't have any left to bang together. And that's one of his favorite pastimes—banging pots and pans together. A person can get an awful headache listening to that racket.

Right after lunch my mother opened up the dinner table. We don't have a separate dining room. When we have company for dinner we eat in one end of the living room. When Mom finished setting the table she put a silver bowl filled with flowers right in the middle. I said, "Hey, Mom . . . it looks like you're expecting the President or something."

"Very funny, Peter!" my mother answered.

Sometimes my mother laughs like crazy at my jokes. Other times she pretends not to get them. And then, there are times when I know she gets them but she doesn't seem to like them. This was one of those times. So I decided no more jokes until after dinner.

I went to Jimmy Fargo's for the afternoon. I came home at four o'clock. I found my mother standing over the dinner table mumbling. Fudge was on the floor playing with my father's socks. I'm not sure why he likes socks so much, but if you give him a few pairs he'll play quietly for an hour.

I said, "Hi, Mom. I'm home."

"I'm missing two flowers," my mother said.

I don't know how she noticed that two flowers were missing from her silver bowl. Because there were at least a dozen of them left. But sure enough, when I checked, I saw two stems with nothing on them.

"Don't look at me, Mom," I said. "What would I do with two measly flowers?"

So we both looked at Fudge. "Did you take Mommy's pretty flowers?" my mother asked him.

"No take," Fudge said. He was chewing on something.

"What's in your mouth?" my mother asked.

Fudge didn't answer.

"Show Mommy!"

"No show," Fudge said.

"Oh yes!" My mother picked him up and forced his mouth open. She fished out a rose petal.

"What did you do with Mommy's flowers?" She raised her voice. She was really getting upset.

Fudge laughed.

"Tell Mommy!"

"Yum!" Fudge said. "Yummy yummy yummy!"

"Oh no!" my mother cried, rushing to the telephone.

She called Dr. Cone. She told him that Fudge ate two flowers. Dr. Cone must have asked what kind, because my mother said, "Roses, I think. But I can't be sure. One might have been a daisy."

There was a long pause while my mother listened to whatever Dr. Cone had to say. Then Mom said, "Thank you, Dr. Cone." She hung up.

"No more flowers!" she told Fudge. "You understand?"

"No more," Fudge repeated. "No more . . . no more . . . no more."

My mother gave him a spoonful of peppermint-flavored medicine. The kind I take when I have stomach pains. Then she carried Fudge off to have his bath.

Leave it to my brother to eat flowers! I wondered how they tasted. *Maybe they're delicious and I don't know it because I've never tasted one,* I thought. I decided to find out. I picked off one petal from a pink rose. I put it in my mouth and tried to chew it up. But I couldn't do it. It tasted awful. I spit it out in the garbage. Well, at least now I knew I wasn't missing anything great!

Fudge ate his supper in the kitchen before our company arrived. While he was eating I heard my mother remind him, "Fudgie's going to be a good boy tonight. Very good for Daddy's friends."

"Good," Fudge said. "Good boy."

"That's right!" my mother told him.

I changed and scrubbed up while Fudge finished his supper. I was going to eat with the company. Being nine has its advantages!

My mother was all dressed up by the time my father got home with the Yarbys. You'd never have guessed that Mom spent most of the day in the kitchen. You'd also never have guessed that Fudge ate two flowers. He was feeling fine. He even smelled nice—like baby powder.

Mrs. Yarby picked him up right away. I knew she would. She looked like a grandmother. That type always makes a big deal out of Fudge. She walked into the living room cuddling him. Then she sat down on the sofa and bounced Fudge around on her lap.

"Isn't he the cutest little boy!" Mrs. Yarby said. "I just love babies." She gave him a big kiss on the top of his head. I kept waiting for somebody to tell her Fudge was no baby. But no one did.

My father carried the Yarbys' suitcase into Fudge's room. When he came back he introduced me to our company.

"This is our older son, Peter," he said to the Yarbys.

"I'm nine and in fourth grade," I told them.

"How do, Peter," Mr. Yarby said.

Mrs. Yarby just gave me a nod. She was still busy with Fudge. "I have a surprise for this dear little boy!" she said. "It's in my suitcase. Should I go get it?"

"Yes," Fudge shouted. "Go get . . . go get!"

Mrs. Yarby laughed, as if that was the best joke she ever heard. "I'll be right back," she told Fudge. She put him down and ran off to find her suitcase.

She came back carrying a present tied up with a red ribbon.

"Ohhhh!" Fudge cried, opening his eyes wide. "Goody!"
He clapped his hands.

Mrs. Yarby helped him unwrap his surprise. It was a
windup train that made a lot of noise. Every time it bumped
into something it turned around and went the other way.
Fudge liked it a lot. He likes anything that's noisy.

I said, "That's a nice train."

Mrs. Yarby turned to me. "Oh, I have something for you too uh . . . uh. . . ."

"Peter," I reminded her. "My name is Peter."

"Yes. Well, I'll go get it."

Mrs. Yarby left the room again. This time she came back with a flat package. It was wrapped up too—red ribbon and all. She handed it to me. Fudge stopped playing with his train long enough to come over and see what I got. I took off the paper very carefully in case my mother wanted to save it. And also to show Mrs. Yarby that I'm a lot more careful about things than my brother. I'm not sure she noticed. My present turned out to be a big picture dictionary. The kind I liked when I was about four years old. My old one is in Fudge's bookcase now.

"I don't know much about big boys," Mrs. Yarby said. "So the lady in the store said a nice book would be a good idea."

A nice book would have been a good idea, I thought. *But a picture dictionary! That's for babies!* I've had my own regular dictionary since I was eight. But I knew I had to be polite so I said, "Thank you very much. It's just what I've always wanted."

"I'm so glad!" Mrs. Yarby said. She let out a long sigh and sat back on the sofa.

My father offered the Yarbys a drink.

"Good idea . . . good idea," Mr. Yarby said.

"What'll it be?" my father asked.

"What'll it be?" Mr. Yarby repeated, laughing. "What do you think, Hatcher? It'll be Juicy-O! That's all we ever drink. Good for your health!" Mr. Yarby pounded his chest.

"Of course!" my father said, like he knew it all along. "Juicy-O for everyone!" my father told my mother. She went into the kitchen to get it.

While my father and Mr. Yarby were discussing Juicy-O, Fudge disappeared. Just as my mother served everyone a glass of Mr. Yarby's favorite drink he came back. He was carrying a book—my old, worn-out picture dictionary. The same as the one the Yarbys just gave me.

"See," Fudge said, climbing up on Mrs. Yarby's lap. "See book."

I wanted to vanish. I think my mother and father did too.

"See book!" Now Fudge held it up over his head.

"I can use another one," I explained. "I really can. That old one is falling apart." I tried to laugh.

"It's returnable," Mrs. Yarby said. "It's silly to keep it if you already have one." She sounded insulted. Like it was my fault she brought me something I already had.

"MINE!" Fudge said. He closed the book and held it tight against his chest. "MINE . . . MINE . . . MINE. . . ."

"It's the thought that counts," my mother said. "It was so nice of you to think of our boys." Then she turned to Fudge. "Put the book away now, Fudgie."

"Isn't it Fudgie's bedtime?" my father hinted.

"Oh yes. I think it is," my mother said, scooping him up. "Say goodnight, Fudgie."

"Goodnight Fudgie!" my brother said, waving at us.

Fudge was supposed to fall asleep before we sat down to dinner. But just in case, my mother put a million little toys in his crib to keep him busy. I don't know who my mother thought she was fooling. Because we all know that Fudge can climb out of his crib any old time he wants to.

He stayed away until we were in the middle of our roast beef. Then he came in carrying Dribble's bowl. He walked right up to Mrs. Yarby. He thought she was his new friend. "See," he said, holding Dribble under her nose. "See Dribble."

Mrs. Yarby shrieked. "Ohhhh! I can't stand reptiles. Get that thing away from me!"

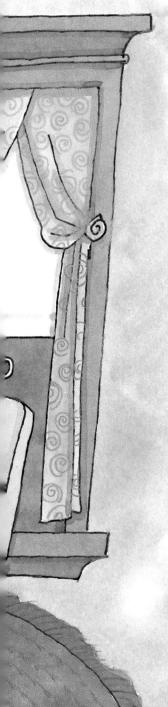

Fudge looked disappointed. So he showed Dribble to Mr. Yarby. "See," he said.

"HATCHER!" Mr. Yarby boomed. "Make him get that thing out of here!"

I wondered why Mr. Yarby called my father "Hatcher." Didn't he know his first name was Warren? And I didn't like the way Mr. and Mrs. Yarby both called Dribble a "thing."

I jumped up. "Give him to me!" I told Fudge. I took Dribble and his bowl and marched into my room. I inspected my turtle all over. He seemed all right. I didn't want to make a big scene in front of our company but I was mad! I mean *really* mad! That kid knows he's not allowed to touch my turtle!

"Peter," my father called, "come and finish your dinner."

When I got back to the table I heard Mrs. Yarby say, "It must be interesting to have children. We never had any ourselves."

"But if we did," Mr. Yarby told my father, "we'd teach them some manners! I'm a firm believer in old-fashioned good manners!"

"So are we, Howard," my mother said in a weak voice.

I thought Mr. Yarby had a lot of nerve to hint that we had no manners. Didn't I pretend to like their dumb old picture dictionary? If that isn't good manners, then I don't know what is!

My mother excused herself and carried Fudge back to my room. I guess she put him into his crib again. I hoped she told him to keep his hands off my things.

We didn't hear from him again until dessert. Just as my mother was pouring the coffee he ran in wearing my rubber gorilla mask from last Hallowe'en. It's a very real-looking mask. I guess that's why Mrs. Yarby screamed so loud. If she hadn't made so much noise my mother probably wouldn't have spilled the coffee all over the floor.

My father grabbed Fudge and pulled the gorilla mask off him. "That's not funny, Fudge!" he said.

"Funny," Fudge laughed. "Funny, funny, funny Fudgie!"

"Yes sir, Hatcher!" Mr. Yarby said. "Old-fashioned manners!"

By that time I'm sure my father was sorry the Yarbys weren't staying at a hotel.

I finally got to bed at ten. Fudge was in his crib slurping away. I thought I'd never fall asleep! But I guess I did. I woke up once, when Fudge started babbling. He said, "Boo-ba-mum-mum-ha-ba-shi." Whatever that means. I didn't even get scared. I whispered, "Shut up!" And he did.

Early the next morning I felt something funny on my arm. At first I didn't wake up. I just felt this little tickle. I thought it was part of my dream. But then I had the feeling somebody was staring at me. So I opened my eyes.

Fudge was standing over me and Dribble was crawling around on my arm. I guess Fudge could tell I was about ready to kill him because he bent down and kissed me. That's what he does when my mother's angry at him. He thinks nobody can resist him when he makes himself so lovable. And a lot of times it works with my mother. But not with me! I jumped up, put Dribble back into his bowl, and smacked Fudge on his backside. *Hard*. He hollered.

My father came running into my room. He was still in his pajamas.

He whispered, "What's going on in here?"

I pointed at Fudge and he pointed at me.

My father picked up my brother and carried him off. "Go back to sleep, Peter," he said. "It's only six o'clock in the morning."

I fell asleep for another hour, then woke up to an awful noise. It was Fudge playing with his new train. It woke up everybody, including the Yarbys. But this time there was nobody they could blame. They were the ones who gave Fudge the train in the first place.

Breakfast was a quiet affair. Nobody had much to say. Mr. Yarby drank two glasses of Juicy-O. Then he told my father that he and Mrs. Yarby had their suitcases packed. They were leaving for a hotel as soon as breakfast was over.

My father said he understood. That the apartment was too small for so many people. My mother didn't say anything.

When Mr. Yarby went into Fudge's bedroom to pick up his suitcase his voice boomed. "HATCHER!"

My father ran toward the bedroom. My mother and Mrs. Yarby followed him. I followed them. When we got there we saw Fudge sitting on the Yarbys' suitcase. He had decorated it with about one hundred green stamps. The kind my mother gets at the supermarket.

"See," Fudge said. "See . . . pretty." He laughed. Nobody else did. Then he licked the last green stamp and stuck it right in the middle of the suitcase. "All gone!" Fudge sang, holding up his hands.

It took my mother half an hour to peel off her trading stamps and clean up the Yarbys' suitcase.

The next week my father came home from the office and collected all the cans of Juicy-O in our house. He dumped them into the garbage. My mother felt bad that my father had lost such an important account. But my father told her not to worry. Juicy-O wasn't selling very well at the stores. Nobody seemed to like the combination of oranges, grapefruits, pineapples, pears, and bananas.

"You know, Dad," I said. "I only drank Juicy-O to be polite. I really hated it!"

"You know something funny, Peter?" my father said. "I thought it was pretty bad myself!"

SOURCE

SCHOLASTIC NEWS

News
Magazine

Laughing is Good for You!

AWARD WINNING Magazine

by Karen Burns
illustrated by Tim Haggerty

Imagine that you've had a really stressful day. You didn't do so hot on your history test. You forgot your gym clothes. And, to make matters worse, Dad packed liverwurst in your lunch!

How do you beat the stress and brighten up your day? Maybe a really great joke or a funny movie will do the trick. Doctors have been studying what happens inside our bodies when we laugh. They believe that getting the giggles can help us beat stress and stay healthy. Here's why:

When you first start to laugh, your heart beats very quickly. But after a few seconds, your heartbeat slows down a lot. That makes you feel very relaxed. Some doctors also think that when you laugh, your brain makes chemicals

called endorphins (en-DOOR-fins). These chemicals may help kill pain and make you feel happy. A good belly laugh is also good exercise for your heart. Experts say that laughing about 100 times a day gives your heart the same workout as rowing a boat for ten minutes!

For hospitals and nursing homes, this is news to smile about. Many of these places are starting to use clowns and carts full of comedy tapes, funny games, and joke books to help their patients get better. Kids know the power of humor, too. Fourth graders in Oceanside, New York, recently wrote a book full of comics, limericks, and jokes for patients in a local nursing home.

So remember, a few laughs a day can keep the doctor away.

Robb Armstrong

Cartoonist

Making people *laugh* is all in a *day's work*.

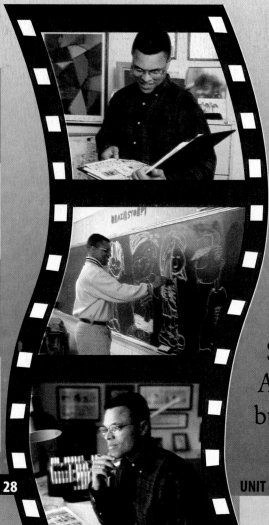

Robb Armstrong is a cartoonist whose comic strip "Jump Start" appears in 150 newspapers across the country. During the day, Armstrong is an art director at an advertising agency. Mornings, evenings, and weekends he draws his comic strip. He has deadlines each week, when all his strips for the following week have to be handed in. The Joe and Marcy characters in "Jump Start" may lead busy lives, but Armstrong is kept even busier creating them.

PROFILE

Name: Robb Armstrong

Occupation: cartoonist and art director

Favorite cartoon characters in fourth grade: Fred Flintstone and Snoopy

Childhood idol: Charles Schulz, creator of "Peanuts"

Cartoon created in fourth grade: "Praying Mantis Man," an African-American superhero

Funniest joke: "Never mind. It's so dumb, my wife leaves the room every time I tell it."

29

QUESTIONS

for Robb Armstrong

Find out how Robb Armstrong turned a talent for drawing into a career.

Q How did you become interested in being a cartoonist?

A I began drawing when I was four years old. Like many kids, I loved to draw, and I decided to stick with it. When I was 17, I sold some political cartoons to the *Philadelphia Tribune*. I thought I had found an easy career. It wasn't until later that I realized how much work it would take to be a professional cartoonist.

Q Did you continue to draw cartoons in college?

A When I went to Syracuse University, I worked on the school paper, *The Daily Orange*. I did a strip called "Hector." Having to draw a comic strip every day meant that I had to be organized and self-disciplined. The experience taught me a lot and helped me later in life.

Q Is it difficult to get a new comic strip published?

A It took me a good ten years to achieve any kind of success. The field of syndicated comics—comics which appear in newspapers all over the country—is very competitive. I finally got a yearlong development deal with United Features Syndicate. This meant I had a year in which to come up with a successful strip.

Q Why do you like to visit schools and talk about your career?

A I enjoy visiting schools almost as much as drawing. I want kids to know that they can have dreams. I tell them that everyone has a talent— that's the easy part. Building a talent, that's what takes hard work.

Q How did you think up the characters Joe and Marcy?

A My editor suggested I think about characters that I know best. Eventually, I drew the characters Joe and Marcy, a young black couple with busy careers. Joe might be a cop and Marcy a nurse, but they're a lot like me and my wife, Sherry.

Q Where do your ideas for jokes in the strip come from?

A Sometimes an idea comes from radio or TV. But I think the best ideas come from life.

Robb Armstrong's
Tips for Cartoon Ideas

1 Watch how people act in different situations.

2 Listen to the way people talk, the stories they tell one another. What makes them laugh?

3 Keep a list of things that you find funny. Can you create a joke from an item on your list?

EARTH HOUNDS

AWARD
WINNING

Book

as explained by
Professor Xargle

Translated into Human by Jeanne Willis
Illustrated by Tony Ross

Good morning, class.
Today we are going to learn about Earth Hounds.

Earth Hounds have tusks in the front and a waggler at the back.

To find the tusks, dangle a sausage at each end.

Earth Hounds have buttons for eyes, a sniffer with two holes, and a built-in necktie.

They use their necktie to lick their underbellies and also the icicle cups of Earthlets who are not looking.

Earth Hounds can stand on four legs, three legs, and two legs. They can jump as high as a roast beef.

For dinner, they consume wigglemeat, skeleton biscuits, a flying snow muffin, a helping of living room rug, and a sock that is four days old.

After this feast they must be taken to a place called walkies, which has many steel trees.

The Earth Hound is attached to a string so that he can be pulled along in a sitting position.

In the park the Earthling finds a piece of tree and hurls it back and forth. The Earth Hound is made to fetch it.

Then the Earthling takes a bouncing rubber sphere and flings it into the pond.

Now the Earthling must fetch it.

The Earth Hound arrives back at the Earth Dwelling and rests under the bed covering of the Earthling.

Earth Hounds hate the hot water bowl. They tuck their wagglers between their legs and make a *Wooo-Woooooo* noise.
Once free, they dry themselves on piles of compost.

Here is a baby Earth Hound, or Houndlet, asleep in the nocturnal footwear of an Earthling.

The Earthling has placed many newspapers on the floor for the Houndlet to read.

That is the end of today's lesson.

If you are all very good, we will visit Planet Earth to play with a real Houndlet.

Those of you who would like to bring your own pets along
should sit at the back of the spaceship.

How to
Write a Fractured Fairy Tale

The fairy godmother is a young girl instead of an older woman.

Many fairy tales begin with "Once upon a time" and end with "happily ever after." What would happen if you turned a fairy tale into a fractured fairy tale?

What is a fractured fairy tale? A fractured fairy tale is a fairy tale with a twist. For example, what would happen if the Three Little Pigs became Three Big Dinosaurs, or if Sleeping Beauty decided to go back to sleep? Sometimes changing the setting is enough to add a humorous twist to the story.

Instead of a ball at the palace, there's a party at a disco.

"Biff E
To the

In this story, Cinderella is a boy called Prince Cinders.

Prince Cinders wears modern clothes.

"All your wishes shall be granted," cried the fairy. "Ziz Ziz Boom, Tic Tac Ta, This empty can shall be a car."

Bang Bong, Bo Bo Bo, disco you shall go!"

The fairy godmother turns an empty can into a car, instead of turning a pumpkin into a coach.

1 Choose a Fairy Tale

On your own, make a list of fairy tales that you've read or heard. If you need ideas, look through a book of fairy tales and skim the stories you know well. Read a few new ones, too. Then choose your favorite.

TOOLS

- book of fairy tales
- pencil and paper
- ruler

2 Make a Story Chart

Chart the important details of the fairy tale you chose. Who are the characters? What is the setting? What happens in the story? Study your chart, and then pick a detail or two that you would like to change. Be sure to write down any substitutions you make on your chart.

	Fairy Tale	My version
Characters	Goldilocks 3 Bears	Goldzilla The Bear Family (people)
Setting	House in woods	House in suburbs

3 Write Your Fractured Fairy Tale

If you like, begin with the traditional fairy tale opening, "Once upon a time. . . ." Use your story chart as an outline. Then rewrite the fairy tale in your own words, using your funny new twist. Are you smiling or laughing as you write? That's a sign that your audience will laugh, too. Be sure to use dialogue. It will make the story more lively.

Tips
- Change the time period of the story.
- Change the setting.
- Have a character in the fairy tale narrate the story.
- Change the characters in the story.
- Change the ending of the story.

4 Present Your Fairy Tale

When you've finished writing your fairy tale:

- Read it aloud to the class.
- Create a class book of fractured fairy tales.
- Work with a small group to turn some of the fractured fairy tales into a series of one-act plays. Invite another class to see your performance.

If You Are Using a Computer . . .

Type your fractured fairy tale on the computer, using the Sign format. Choose a border and clip art to illustrate your story.

THINK

Why does a fairy tale become humorous when you change an important part of the story?

Robb Armstrong
Cartoonist ▶

Surprise and exaggeration can make things seem funny.

What's So Funny?

Join Arthur as he tries to buy a turkey and ends up with a surprise.

Tickle your funny bone with poems and limericks.

Find out what happens when a mule decides to speak.

Meet the strongest woman in the West.

WORKSHOP 2

Make yourself laugh by writing a humorous poem.

Oodles of Noodles

I love noodles. Give me oodles.
Make a mound up to the sun.
Noodles are my favorite foodles.
I eat noodles by the ton.

Lucia and James L. Hymes, Jr.

from

The Hoboken Chicken Emergency

A Television Script
by Arthur Alsberg and Don Nelson
illustrated by Rick Brown

Based on the novel by
Daniel Manus Pinkwater

AWARD WINNING
Author

INTERIOR—BOBOWICZ LIVING ROOM—NIGHT

[POPPA snaps off the TV set as MOMMA enters, followed by ARTHUR. He reaches into his pocket and pulls out twenty dollars, which he hands to ARTHUR.]

POPPA
Arthur, that's for tomorrow morning. To pick up a turkey at O'Brien's.

MOMMA
Carl . . . How can I fit a turkey in the ice box for two weeks?

POPPA
I'm not taking any chances, and no mistakes like last year, Arthur.

ARTHUR
Why couldn't we have something else? Maybe meatloaf.

POPPA
In America, on Thanksgiving, it's turkey. Every family in the neighborhood will want a turkey—the Antonellis, the Glucksterns, the Lings, [indicating himself] . . . and the Bobowiczs. It's an American tradition.

ARTHUR
I'd rather have pizza.

POPPA

[firmly] When your grandparents were young and
still in Poland, if someone said "eat turkey" they'd
have to eat turkey. Here in America we have a
choice. [firmly] And the choice is turkey!

EXTERIOR—PARK AND PLAYGROUND—MORNING

[ARTHUR is trudging through the park where he sees three boys playing on
the swing, some distance from him.]

ARTHUR

[calling] Hey George! Hi, Benny!

[He waves, but the three boys continue swinging and don't even look over at
ARTHUR. ARTHUR waits a moment . . . maybe they didn't hear him.]

ARTHUR

[calling again] Mario! Want to come to the butcher
with me?

MARIO

[calling] I can't!

[The boys continue swinging, and ARTHUR turns and walks along the fence
and out of the park.]

EXTERIOR—HOBOKEN STREET—MORNING

[ARTHUR stands in front of O'Brien's Meat Market. He tries the door, but it
is locked. He peers through the window, but no one is inside. There is a sign
in the window of the door—CLOSED BECAUSE OF A DEATH IN THE FAMILY.]

[He finally turns away, wondering what to do. Suddenly some large feathers come floating down from above. They are accompanied by a clucking sound coming from off stage. ARTHUR looks around. The clucking is not like any clucking he has ever heard before. It's deeper and louder. ARTHUR looks up toward an apartment above the meat market.]

ANOTHER ANGLE

[The second story window of the apartment. PROFESSOR MAZZOCCHI, a wild-eyed, slightly frazzled older man is leaning out the window, backwards, as if preventing something from jumping out. He notices ARTHUR in the street below.]

PROFESSOR

[calling down] Nothing to fear. Everything's under control.

[The PROFESSOR then directs his attention into the room.]

PROFESSOR

[continuing] Back! Back, Number 73!

ANGLE ON ARTHUR

[He looks up at the PROFESSOR.]

ARTHUR

Are you the butcher?

ANGLE ON PROFESSOR

PROFESSOR

[indignantly] Butcher? Me? Doctor Frankenstein was a butcher! I am a scientist!

ANGLE ON ARTHUR

ARTHUR

I came to buy our Thanksgiving turkey, but they're
closed.

ANGLE ON PROFESSOR

PROFESSOR

[his eyes widen] Money? You have some money?
Press the button next to the name "Professor
Mazzocchi."

[The PROFESSOR is distracted for a moment as he pushes something back
into the room with his foot. Then he turns back toward ARTHUR.]

PROFESSOR

[continuing; calling down] But hurry! They're going
fast!

ANGLE ON ARTHUR

[ARTHUR considers the offer, then hurries over to the entrance to the
apartment building. He looks at the card near the doorway. It reads:
PROFESSOR MAZZOCCHI—INVENTOR OF THE CHICKEN SYSTEM—BY
APPOINTMENT. ARTHUR presses the button. In a moment the buzzer sounds
to release the door. ARTHUR pushes it and enters the building.]

INTERIOR—APARTMENT LOBBY—DAY

[ARTHUR starts up the stairs but is frozen by the sound of PROFESSOR
MAZZOCCHI's voice.]

PROFESSOR (off stage)

[shouting] You will not get me evicted! My brother owns this building! I'm a scientist! If you people don't stop bothering me, I'll let the rooster loose again!

ARTHUR

[puzzled, calls] But you told me to come in.

PROFESSOR (off stage)

[realizes] Oh, it's you, my boy. Come right up. What are you waiting for?

INTERIOR HALL—TOP OF THE STAIRS—DAY

[The PROFESSOR, wearing an old bathrobe with dragons embroidered on it, greets ARTHUR as he comes up.]

PROFESSOR

The only people who ever come up here are neighbors to complain about my chickens. They don't want me to keep them.

ARTHUR

You keep chickens in your apartment?

PROFESSOR

A farm would be better, but my brother lets me stay here without paying any rent. Also, they are special chickens. I prefer to keep them under lock and key.

ARTHUR

I was supposed to get a turkey.

PROFESSOR

Do you have a large family?

ARTHUR

No, sir.

PROFESSOR

But your family has friends . . .

ARTHUR

Yes, sir. We live in a big apartment building.

PROFESSOR

Splendid! Perfect for number 73—my super chicken.

ARTHUR

My father wants a turkey.

PROFESSOR

In the spirit of Thanksgiving wouldn't your father rather feed his family and all his friends and neighbors for only . . . [stops] How much money have you got?

ARTHUR

Twenty dollars.

[ARTHUR takes the twenty dollar bill out of his pocket.]

PROFESSOR

[continuing] Just enough. Wait here.

[The PROFESSOR opens the door just enough to slide through it and closes it, leaving ARTHUR standing outside. ARTHUR stands patiently for a moment, then stirs uneasily as he hears the same loud, low clucking sound he'd heard before. Suddenly the door swings open and the PROFESSOR comes out of the apartment leading a huge chicken, taller than he is, on a leash. The CHICKEN has a look of wide-eyed innocence about her.]

PROFESSOR

The best poultry bargain on earth! One medium-sized super chicken—eight cents a pound. Here's Number 73, your two hundred and sixty-six pound super chicken.

ARTHUR

But I was supposed to get a turkey.

PROFESSOR

When I'm offering you a super chicken? Just look at this fine specimen. Good for roasting, frying, and barbecuing.

[At the sound of this the CHICKEN begins to tremble all over.]

ARTHUR

But what about my father?

PROFESSOR

Well, take it or leave it. I can always sell her to a Kiwanis picnic or the Coast Guard mess.

[ARTHUR hesitates. The CHICKEN seems to moan.]

PROFESSOR

She'll be mighty good eating.

[The CHICKEN looks over toward ARTHUR, almost pleading.]

ARTHUR

Well . . .

PROFESSOR

[quickly] A deal!

[He snaps the twenty dollars from ARTHUR's fingers and hands him the leash.]

PROFESSOR

And I'll throw in the collar and leash.

[The PROFESSOR opens the door of his apartment and disappears. ARTHUR stands there for a moment then looks up at the CHICKEN. The CHICKEN shifts from foot to foot looking rather nervous. ARTHUR, realizing his mistake, pounds on the apartment door.]

PROFESSOR (off stage)

[shouts] No refunds!

ARTHUR

Don't you have anything smaller?

PROFESSOR (off stage)

No refunds!

[ARTHUR shakes his head and looks up at the CHICKEN.]

ARTHUR

I hope Poppa likes bargains.

[He starts to lead the CHICKEN away.]

EXTERIOR—PARK AND PLAYGROUND—MORNING

[ARTHUR leads the CHICKEN along the walk as he searches the park for the three boys he had seen earlier. But the swings are empty, and no one is in sight. With a little shrug, ARTHUR accepts his lonely fate and crosses the street toward home, an old brick building with a fire escape on the outside.]

INTERIOR—APARTMENT BUILDING HALLWAY—DAY

[ARTHUR is leading the CHICKEN who follows him tamely as they climb the stairs to the second floor. ARTHUR starts down the hallway toward his apartment, then looks at the CHICKEN and stops. He has second thoughts.]

ARTHUR

[to CHICKEN] You better wait here.

[ARTHUR ties the CHICKEN to the banister and then goes to the door of his apartment. He stops and thinks for a moment. Then he enters.]

INTERIOR—BOBOWICZ LIVING ROOM—DAY

[MOMMA BOBOWICZ is vacuuming as ARTHUR enters. MOMMA looks up but continues vacuuming.]

MOMMA

What took you so long? I was starting to get worried.

ARTHUR

Are you in a good mood or a bad mood?

[ARTHUR'S MOTHER looks up at ARTHUR suspiciously then turns off the vacuum cleaner.]

MOMMA

Arthur. You didn't lose the twenty dollars?

ARTHUR

[defensively] No.

MOMMA

Good.

[ARTHUR'S MOTHER turns on the vacuum again and starts cleaning.]

ARTHUR

Not exactly.

[ARTHUR'S MOTHER turns the vacuum off again.]

MOMMA

Exactly what did you do?

ARTHUR

I got a chicken.

MOMMA

You what?

ARTHUR

You *are* in a bad mood.

MOMMA

[softening] Well, where is it?

ARTHUR

I left it in the hall. It only cost eight cents a pound.

MOMMA

That's very cheap. Are you sure there's nothing wrong with it? Maybe it isn't fresh?

ARTHUR

It's fresh all right.

[MOMMA BOBOWICZ opens the door to reveal the CHICKEN standing in the hallway tied to the banister. The CHICKEN looks toward her and clucks! MOMMA BOBOWICZ quickly closes the door and just stands there facing the closed door—speechless for a moment.]

MOMMA

There's a two hundred pound chicken in the hall!

ARTHUR

[nervously] Two hundred and sixty-six pounds.

[MOMMA BOBOWICZ is still looking at the door.]

MOMMA

Two hundred and sixty-six pounds of live chicken!
It's wearing a dog collar.

[MOMMA BOBOWICZ opens the door just a crack, peeks out, then quickly closes the door again.]

MOMMA

[continuing] It's there, all right.

[She turns toward ARTHUR accusingly.]

ARTHUR

[close to tears] I couldn't help it, Momma. I got it
from this old scientist. He was saying it was a
bargain, and I didn't know what to do.

[MOMMA BOBOWICZ looks at her son who is on the verge of tears. She then opens the door again and looks into the hall.]

ANGLE ON HALL

[The CHICKEN stands shifting from one foot to the other.]

ANGLE ON LIVING ROOM

[MOMMA closes the door again.]

ARTHUR
I thought we could call her "Henrietta."

MOMMA
We're not calling her anything! That twenty dollars
was for a turkey to eat, not a two hundred sixty-six
pound chicken to keep as a pet.

ARTHUR
[fighting the tears] But we can't take her back or that
old man is gonna feed her to the Coast Guard or
some people at a picnic. Momma, please.

[MOMMA BOBOWICZ looks at ARTHUR for a moment, thinking it over.
Then she opens the door again and looks out into the hallway.]

ANGLE ON HALLWAY

[The CHICKEN looks toward MOMMA and cocks its head.]

ANGLE ON LIVING ROOM

[MOMMA looks out toward the CHICKEN and softens a bit.]

MOMMA
She does seem friendly, in a dumb sort of way.

[ARTHUR senses his mother's change of attitude.]

ARTHUR

I'd feed her and walk her and take care of her. I
could train her so she'd cluck if burglars ever came.

MOMMA

Well . . .

ARTHUR

Please, Momma. She's a good chicken. And I'd do
everything.

MOMMA

Who's going to tell your father?

ARTHUR

You could do that.

[ARTHUR looks at his mother innocently. She shakes her head and smiles.
It's the signal for ARTHUR to hug her gratefully.]

INTERIOR—DINING ROOM—NIGHT

[ARTHUR is seated at the dinner table with his parents. POPPA BOBOWICZ
is definitely in a bad mood.]

POPPA

You think I make money just to throw it away?

ARTHUR

I'm sorry, Poppa. I didn't mean to.

MOMMA

It's such an unusual pet, Carl. And psychologists
say it's good for the children when the family has
a pet.

POPPA

Dr. Freud should raise a family on my salary.

[ARTHUR gets up and hurries from the room.]

MOMMA

There'll still be time to get the turkey. Besides, with what they're paying for pets these days, the chicken's a bargain. [slyly] And everybody looks for bargains. It's the American way.

POPPA

[seeing through it] The American way is a turkey on the table at Thanksgiving, not a two hundred pound chicken on a leash!

ANOTHER ANGLE TO INCLUDE ARTHUR AS HE ENTERS WITH HENRIETTA ON THE LEASH.

ARTHUR

I'll take her back if that's what you want, Poppa.

[POPPA looks at MOMMA. She looks back, beseechingly.]

POPPA

[weakening] Well, we'll see.

[ARTHUR exchanges smiles with his mother. Then he pats HENRIETTA. HENRIETTA looks down at a dinner plate with French fries on it. ARTHUR holds one up for her to eat and she gobbles it down.]

POPPA

[sternly] And no feeding pets from the table.

[ARTHUR and his MOTHER react at the word "pets."]

INTERIOR—ARTHUR'S ROOM—NIGHT

[ARTHUR, in his pajamas, is standing on his bed as he talks to HENRIETTA who stands on the floor.]

ARTHUR

I've never had a chicken for a pet before. I've never even had a pet. Poppa doesn't like pets. He says they're a lot of trouble. But maybe he'll change his mind.

[HENRIETTA just looks at ARTHUR and clucks.]

ARTHUR

Come on. Jump up.

[HENRIETTA doesn't budge.]

ARTHUR

[continuing] Up on the bed, Henrietta. Up on the bed!

[HENRIETTA turns absently and starts to walk away. ARTHUR turns and closes the closet door. Startled, HENRIETTA turns and jumps on the bed. The bed collapses. ARTHUR shakes his head in dismay.]

CAMERA TERMS

DISSOLVE	the gradual replacement of one shot with another
EXTERIOR	a view of an outdoor scene
INTERIOR	a view of an indoor scene
ANGLE	the camera's point of view as it films its subject

from
Poems of A. Nonny Mouse

As I was walking round the lake,
I met a little rattlesnake.
I gave him so much ice-cream cake,
It made his little belly ache.

If you should meet a crocodile,
Don't take a stick and poke him.
Ignore the welcome in his smile,
Be careful not to stroke him.
For as he sleeps upon the Nile,
He thinner gets and thinner.
And whene'er you meet a crocodile,
He's ready for his dinner.

Selected by Jack Prelutsky
Illustrated by Henrik Drescher

A froggie sat on a lily pad,
Looking up at the sky.
The lily pad broke and the frog fell in,
Water all in his eye.

Froggy Boggy
tried to jump
on a stone
and got a bump.

It made his eyes
wink and frown
and turned his nose
upside down.

A centipede was happy quite,
Until a frog in fun
said, "Pray, which leg comes after which?"
This raised her mind to such a pitch,
She lay distracted in the ditch,
Considering how to run.

The Man in the Moon as he sails the sky
Is a very remarkable skipper,
But he made a mistake when he tried to take
A drink of milk from the Dipper.
He dipped right out of the Milky Way
And slowly and carefully filled it.
The Big Bear growled and the Little Bear howled,
And frightened him so that he spilled it!

"Bubble," said the kettle,
"Bubble," said the pot.
"Bubble, bubble, bubble,
We are getting very hot!"

Shall I take you off the fire?
"No, you need not trouble.
This is just the way we talk—
Bubble, bubble, bubble!"

from
FROM SEA TO SHINING SEA
Compiled by Amy L. Cohn

The Talking Mule

COLLECTED BY ZORA NEALE HURSTON

ILLUSTRATED BY DONALD CREWS

Old feller one time had a mule. His name was Bill. Every morning when that old feller went to catch him he'd say, "Come 'round, Bill!"

But one morning he slept late so he decided while he was drinking some coffee that he'd send his son to catch old Bill.

Told his son, "Go down there, boy, and bring that mule up here."

That boy was such a fast aleck he grabbed the bridle and went on down to the lot. When he got there, he said, "Come 'round, Bill!"

The mule looked 'round at the boy. The boy told the mule, " 'Tain't no use rollin' your eyes at me. Pa wants you this morning. Come on 'round and stick your head in this bridle."

The mule kept on looking at him and said, "Every mornin' it's 'Come 'round, Bill! Come 'round, Bill!' I can't hardly rest at night before it's 'Come 'round, Bill!' "

The boy threw down the bridle, flew back to the house, and told his pa, "That mule's talkin'!"

"Oh, come on, boy, tellin' your lies! Go on and catch that mule."

"No, sir, Pa, that mule's started to talk. You'll have to catch that mule all by yourself. I'm not goin' ta do it."

The old feller looked at his wife and said, "Do you see what a lie this boy is tellin'?"

He got up and went on down after the mule himself. When he got down to the lot he hollered, "Come 'round, Bill!"

The old mule looked 'round and said, "Every mornin' it's 'Come 'round, Bill!' "

Now, the old feller had a little dog that followed him everywhere. So when he ran for home the little dog was right behind him. The old feller told his wife, "The boy didn't tell much of a lie! That mule *is* talkin'. I've never heard a mule talk before."

L'il dog said, "Me neither."

The old feller got scared again. Right through the woods he ran with the little dog behind him. He nearly ran himself to death. Finally, he stopped, all out of breath, and said, "I'm so tired I don't know what to do."

The l'il dog caught up, sat right in front of him, panting, and said, "Me neither."

That man is running yet.

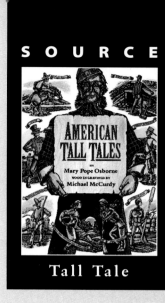
from

American Tall Tales

by Mary Pope Osborne

Wood Engravings by Michael McCurdy

AWARD WINNING

Book

NOTES ON THE STORY

THE BACKWOODS WOMEN of Tennessee and Kentucky
endured the same hardships as the men as they tried to carve a
life out of the wilderness. They helped build cabins and clear
land for planting. They hauled water from springs, grew cotton
for clothes, and hunted wild animals. Though no early tall tales
celebrate an abiding heroine, the Davy Crockett Almanacks do
present rugged frontier women in a number of vignettes, such
as "Sal Fink, the Mississippi Screamer," "Nance Bowers Taming
a Bear," "Katy Goodgrit and the Wolves," and "Sappina Wing
and the Crocodile." In these stories the Davy Crockett
character tells about comically outrageous women who display
amazing boldness and ingenuity.

In the following tale I have chosen to combine these
various female characters into a single heroine—and have
called her Sally Ann Thunder Ann Whirlwind, the name
of Davy's fictional wife, who is briefly mentioned in the
Davy Crockett Almanacks.

One early spring day, when the leaves of the white oaks were about as big as a mouse's ear, Davy Crockett set out alone through the forest to do some bear hunting. Suddenly it started raining real hard, and he felt obliged to stop for shelter under a tree. As he shook the rain out of his coonskin cap, he got sleepy, so he laid back into the crotch of the tree, and pretty soon he was snoring.

Davy slept so hard, he didn't wake up until nearly sundown. And when he did, he discovered that somehow or another in all that sleeping his head had gotten stuck in the crotch of the tree, and he couldn't get it out.

Well, Davy roared loud enough to make the tree lose all its little mouse-ear leaves. He twisted and turned and carried on for over an hour, but still that tree wouldn't let go. Just as he was about to give himself up for a goner, he heard a girl say, "What's the matter, stranger?"

Even from his awkward position, he could see that she was extraordinary—tall as a hickory sapling, with arms as big as a keelboat tiller's.

"My head's stuck, sweetie," he said. "And if you help me get it free, I'll give you a pretty little comb."

"Don't call me sweetie," she said. "And don't worry about giving me no pretty little comb, neither. I'll free your old coconut, but just because I want to."

Then this extraordinary girl did something that made Davy's hair stand on end. She reached in a bag and took out a bunch of rattlesnakes. She tied all the wriggly critters together to make a long rope, and as she tied, she kept talking. "I'm not a shy little colt," she said. "And I'm not a little singing nightingale, neither. I can tote a steamboat on my back, outscream a panther, and jump over my own shadow. I can double up crocodiles any day, and I like to wear a hornets' nest for my Sunday bonnet."

As the girl looped the ends of her snake rope to the top of the branch that was trapping Davy, she kept bragging: "I'm a streak of lightning set up edgeways and buttered with quicksilver. I can outgrin, outsnort, outrun, outlift, outsneeze, outsleep, outlie any varmint from Maine to Louisiana. Furthermore, *sweetie*, I can blow out the moonlight and sing a wolf to sleep." Then she pulled on the other end of the snake rope so hard, it seemed as if she might tear the world apart.

The right-hand fork of that big tree bent just about double. Then Davy slid his head out as easy as you please. For a minute he was so dizzy, he couldn't tell up from down. But when he got everything going straight again, he took a good look at that girl. "What's your name, ma'am?"

"Sally Ann Thunder Ann Whirlwind," she said. "But if you mind your manners, you can call me Sally."

From then on Davy Crockett was crazy in love with Sally Ann Thunder Ann Whirlwind. He asked everyone he knew about her, and everything he heard caused another one of Cupid's arrows to jab him in the gizzard.

"Oh, I know Sally!" the preacher said. "She can dance a rock to pieces and ride a panther bareback!"

"Sally's a good ole friend of mine," the blacksmith said. "Once I seen her crack a walnut with her front teeth."

"Sally's so very special," said the schoolmarm. "She likes to whip across the Salt River, using her apron for a sail and her left leg for a rudder!"

Sally Ann Thunder Ann Whirlwind had a reputation for being funny, too. Her best friend, Lucy, told Davy, "Sally can laugh the bark off a pine tree. She likes to whistle out one side of her mouth while she eats with the other side and grins with the middle!"

According to her friends, Sally could tame about anything in the world, too. They all told Davy about the time she was churning butter and heard something scratching outside. Suddenly the door swung open, and in walked the Great King Bear of the Mud Forest. He'd come to steal one of her smoked hams. Well, before the King Bear could say boo, Sally grabbed a warm dumpling from the pot and stuffed it in his mouth.

The dumpling tasted so good, the King Bear's eyes winked with tears. But then he started to think that Sally might taste pretty good, too. So opening and closing his big old mouth, he backed her right into a corner.

Sally was plenty scared, with her knees a-knocking and her heart a-hammering. But just as the King Bear blew his hot breath in her face, she gathered the courage to say, "Would you like to dance?"

As everybody knows, no bear can resist an invitation to a square dance, so of course the old fellow forgot all about eating Sally and said, "Love to."

Then he bowed real pretty, and the two got to kicking and whooping and swinging each other through the air, as Sally sang:

> *We are on our way to Baltimore,*
> *With two behind, and two before:*
> *Around, around, around we go,*
> *Where oats, peas, beans, and barley grow!*

And while she was singing, Sally tied a string from the bear's ankle to her butter churn, so that all the time the old feller was kicking up his legs and dancing around the room, he was also churning her butter!

And folks loved to tell the story about Sally's encounter with another stinky varmint—only this one was a *human* varmint. It seems that Mike Fink, the riverboat man, decided to scare the toenails off Sally because he was sick and tired of hearing Davy Crockett talk about how great she was.

One evening Mike crept into an old alligator skin and met Sally just as she was taking off to forage in the woods for berries. He spread open his gigantic mouth and made such a howl that he nearly scared himself to death. But Sally paid no more attention to that fool than she would have to a barking puppy dog.

However, when Mike put out his claws to embrace her, her anger rose higher than a Mississippi flood. She threw a flash of eye lightning at him, turning the dark to daylight. Then she pulled out a little toothpick and with a single swing sent the alligator head flying fifty feet! And then to finish him off good, she rolled up her sleeves and knocked Mike Fink clear across the woods and into a muddy swamp.

When the fool came to, Davy Crockett was standing over him. "What in the world happened to you, Mikey?" he asked.

"Well, I—I think I must-a been hit by some kind of wild alligator!" Mike stammered, rubbing his sore head.

Davy smiled, knowing full well it was Sally Ann Thunder Ann Whirlwind just finished giving Mike Fink the only punishment he'd ever known.

That incident caused Cupid's final arrow to jab Davy's gizzard. "Sally's the whole steamboat," he said, meaning she was something great. The next day he put on his best raccoon hat and sallied forth to see her.

When he got within three miles of her cabin, he began to holler her name. His voice was so loud, it whirled through the woods like a hurricane.

Sally looked out and saw the wind a-blowing and the trees a-bending. She heard her name a-thundering through the woods, and her heart began to thump. By now she'd begun to feel that Davy Crockett was the whole steamboat, too. So she put on her best hat—an eagle's nest with a wildcat's tail for a feather—and ran outside.

Just as she stepped out the door, Davy Crockett burst from the woods and jumped onto her porch as fast as a frog. "Sally, darlin'!" he cried. "I think my heart is bustin'! Want to be my wife?"

"Oh, my stars and possum dogs, why not?" she said.

From that day on, Davy Crockett had a hard time acting tough around Sally Ann Thunder Ann Whirlwind. His fightin' and hollerin' had no more effect on her than dropping feathers on a barn floor. At least that's what *she'd* tell you. *He* might say something else.

How to
Write a Funny Poem

There is something about a poem—
a silly, tickle-your-funny-bone,
kick-up-your-feet
kind of poem—that makes
a person grab a pencil and want
to write his or her own.

What is a funny poem? A funny poem
can be rhymed, limericked, rapped,
or have a rhythm all its own.
It can tell a joke, or exaggerate
facts, as long as the end result
makes you laugh.

Oodles of Noodles

I love noodles. Give me oodles.
Make a mound up to the sun.
Noodles are my favorite foodles.
I eat noodles by the ton.

Lucia and James L. Hymes, Jr.

- The subject of the poem can be as silly as you want.

- A poet can create different rhyme patterns. In this poem, lines 1 and 3 have rhymes in them, and lines 2 and 4 rhyme.

A Young Lady of Crete

There was a young lady of Crete,
Who was so exceedingly neat,
When she got out of bed
She stood on her head,
To make sure of not soiling her feet.

Anonymous

- All limericks have the same pattern of rhythm and rhyme.

1 Brainstorm Topics

On your own, brainstorm some funny topics for your poem. Think about jokes and stories you know. Imagine ridiculous situations that could never really happen. And don't forget about everyday situations— even a messy room can be funny if you describe it creatively. (Well, maybe your family wouldn't agree!) Once you have a list of ideas, choose one.

TOOLS

- pencil and paper
- dictionary and thesaurus

2 Pick a Form

Your funny poem can be whatever you want it to be—long or short, a rap or a rhyme, or just a few silly lines. You can write your poem to look like a shape. If your poem is about a bowling ball, try writing it in a circle. If you want to write a limerick, look through poetry books for examples. Think about what you want your poem to say. Then choose the form that you think will work best.

Tip • Try using words that sound funny, such as *boing* or *zing,* or make up words of your own.

3 Write Your Poem

Once you've decided what form you want your poem to take, start writing. When you're finished, read it aloud to yourself. Does it sound flat in places? You may want to change one or two words so that the rhythm is stronger. If you'd like your poem to rhyme (it doesn't have to), here's a hint: Use a rhyming dictionary or a thesaurus to help you find new words.

A hat, it is said, will always have a job. Since it **KNOWS** how to get ahead.

4 Have a Poetry Reading

Have a poetry reading in your classroom. If you prefer, add pictures and make your poem into a greeting card. Send it to a friend who could use a good laugh. You could also combine your poem with others and make a class book.

If You Are Using a Computer...

Use the thesaurus on your computer as you write your poem. You can create banners and posters on the computer to advertise your poetry reading.

THINK

How can the rhyme and rhythm of a poem help make it funny?

Robb Armstrong
Cartoonist ▶

People use humor to entertain each other.

Funny People

Learn how an illustrator turned his talent for doodling into a career.

Travel back in time to a prehistoric land.

Cheer for Amy as she tries to become a riddle champion. Then learn a recipe for making riddles.

PROJECT

Turn a funny situation or joke into a comic strip.

from
**TALKING
WITH ARTISTS**
compiled and edited
by
Pat Cummings

AWARD WINNING

Book

LANE
SMITH

Birthday: August 25, 1959

MY STORY

THE CIRCLE STAGE

I've always doodled and scribbled, but the moment when things really started to click was when I discovered the "Circle Concept." You see, *all* cartoon characters are made up primarily of circles. In fact, a lot of things are. Up until then I just let my pencil wander all over the place, never drawing anything the same way twice. Starting with circles put a little structure into my artwork—and made things a lot easier.

See . . .

Well, the "Circle Concept" worked for *almost* everything.

THE SPACE STAGE

I think one of my fondest memories is of lying stretched out on the library floor at Parkridge Elementary, reading Eleanor Cameron's *Wonderful Flight to the Mushroom Planet.* I loved the story and the art. To this day, whenever I smell hard-boiled eggs I think of how Chuck and David saved the planet with the sulfur-smelling eggs.

From then on I drew only "space stuff."

See . . .

Mr. Space. **Age 8. Pencil and crayon, 5 x 2¾".**

THE OTHER STAGES

Over the years I went through a lot of other stages, too—the CAR AND SUBMARINE STAGE, the BASEBALL STAGE, the SUPERHERO STAGE, the BUG STAGE, and so on.

And each stage had its moments. When I was ten, I made an animated flip-book of a baseball player pitching. When I was fourteen, I sent samples of my superheroes to Marvel Comics and they actually answered back with a letter of encouragement and a free sheet of the official art board that their artists used (Wow! Free paper!).

For a while I was into trees. By the way, have you ever noticed that all trees drawn by kids must have this thing on them? We don't know what makes us draw it, or even what it is, for that matter—it's just something we're born with.

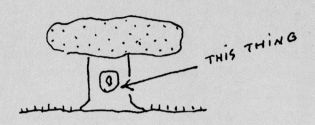

THIS THING

In junior high and high school I received a lot of encouragement from my art teachers. My junior high teacher, Ms. Ng, entered some of my work in an art show and it actually won!!!*

Then in high school, Mr. Baughman convinced me to experiment with different types of materials. I tried acrylics, oil paints, pen and ink, and watercolor. I learned that different media could create different moods (watercolors make great sad-rainy-day pictures).

Mr. Baughman also exposed me to all kinds of art and illustration in books. When I finally did my own book, *Flying Jake*, I dedicated it to him.

I am glad things worked out the way they did and I am able to spend my life drawing pictures for a living. I can't imagine what would've happened if I had decided to become a mathematician.

* "Honorable Mention"

"TO BE AN ARTIST YOU HAVE TO KEEP ON DOING ART—JUST DRAW, DRAW, DRAW!"—LANE SMITH

1. Where do you get your ideas from?

I get my ideas from everything! Like the way somebody parts their hair might give me an idea for a picture of a winding river, or shoestrings in knots can inspire drawings of futuristic highways. Of course if that doesn't work, I just copy the drawings from my comic books.

2. Do you have any children? Any pets?

Yes, I have one child. His name is A.J. He is a cat. He is fat.

3. What do you enjoy drawing the most?

Faces.

4. Do you ever put people you know in your pictures?

Not directly, but elements of them creep into my work, and that big, fat cat in *The Big Pets* looks very familiar.

5. What do you use to make your pictures?

Oil paints, and sometimes I add (collage) real things into my illustrations like sticks, old photos, newspaper clippings, and so on.

I did a book with Jon Scieszka called *The True Story of the Three Little Pigs!* I collaged a bunch of stuff into that one. Jon said, "How creative!" Little did he know it was really saving me a lot of painting time.

Heh, heh.

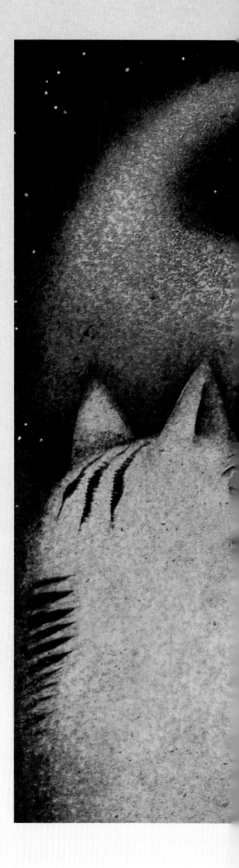

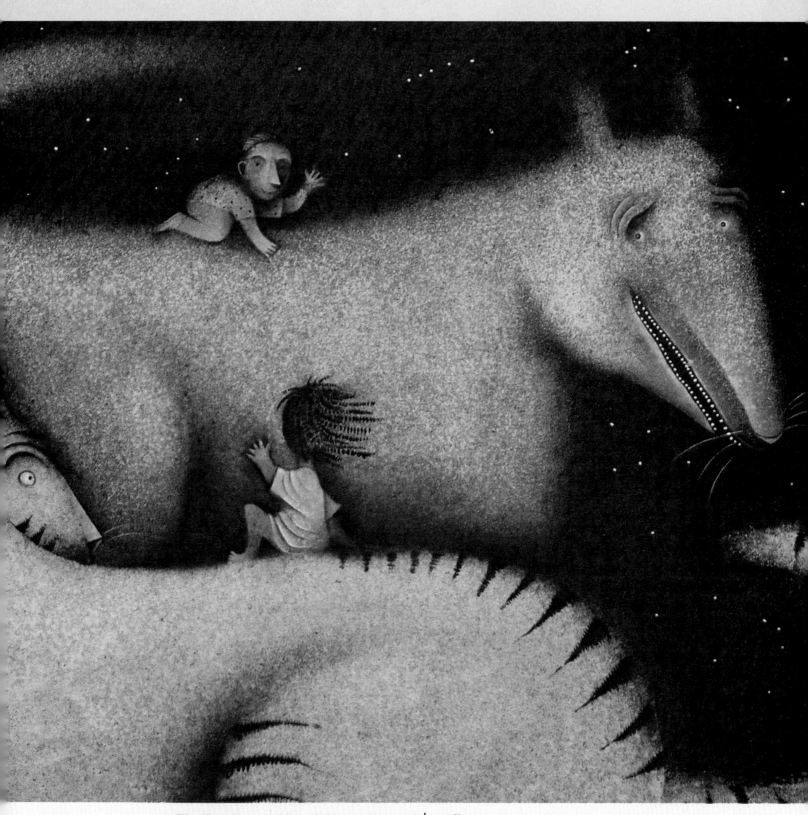

The Big Pets. 1991. Oil painting, $12\frac{1}{2}$ x 9".
Published by Viking Penguin.

from

Your Mother Was a Neanderthal

BY JON SCIESZKA
ILLUSTRATED BY LANE SMITH

In Jon Scieszka's "Time Warp Trio" series, Fred, Sam, and Joe travel back in time and have many comical adventures. This trip finds the three boys in the Stone Age, where they've met a caveman named Duh and his band of hunters. Now the boys are about to meet somebody new.

Trees shook.

Rocks crashed.

The ground wiggled and suddenly split open right behind us.

The cavemen's logpile home fell into the cracked earth and disappeared. Then everything stopped. No birds, no bugs, no prehistoric beasts made a sound.

I sat up and dusted off my animal skin. "That could have been . . . I mean, that was almost . . . we were almost . . ."

"Smashed into little bits and buried under a ton of prehistoric garbage!" screamed Sam.

"Calm down, Sam," said Fred. "Things could be worse."

"Oh yeah? How?" said Sam, looking a little wild-eyed and crazy. "We're trapped 40,000 years in the past. Everything we meet tries to eat us. And now even the ground underneath us is falling apart. And you say things could be worse? How could things be worse?" Sam smacked himself on the forehead with the palm of his hand.

Duh and his men stood up carefully and moved to the edge of the new ravine. They looked down at the pile of broken logs at the bottom. They looked at Sam. Duh let out a wild yell, then smacked himself in the head. And all at once, all of the guys started yelling, moaning, and smacking their heads.

"That's how," said Fred.

Sam yelled. The caveguys yelled. Sam moaned. The caveguys moaned.

"And how," I said.

The noise of Sam, Duh, and the caveguys grew louder and louder, and suddenly *much* louder.

Duh stopped beating himself up, listened, and then yelled something that sounded like "Woo Maa! Woo Maa!" Everyone ran for the trees and left Fred, Sam, and me staring at each other.

"Woo Maa?" said Fred. "What's Woo Maa?"

Sam stood frozen, looking off into the space over our heads.

"I don't know," I said. "But I think we've lost Sam."

Sam croaked, "Woo . . . woo . . . woo . . . ma . . . ma . . . ma—"

"We've definitely lost him," said Fred.

Sam raised his arm to point and croaked again, "Oh, no. Woolly mammoth!"

"He's snapped. He thinks we're the cavewomen," I said. "It's okay, Sam. It's me, Joe."

And right then I was stopped by an earpopping trumpeted blast of noise. Fred and I turned to look behind us. There, standing at the edge of the clearing, not twenty feet away from us, stood the largest and most crazed-looking beast you will never want to see as long as you live. You've seen them in books. And you've seen their relatives in zoos. And I'm telling you, you don't need to see them any closer.

"Oh, no," I said.

"*Woolly mammoth!*" yelled Fred.

At that moment I understood where the word *mammoth* came from. This thing was huge. It was gigantic. Enormous. Mammoth.

The mammoth jerked his head back and fixed us with one tiny eye. Fortunately, he seemed just as surprised to see us as we were to see him. Unfortunately, he stood about ten feet taller and weighed about two tons more than us. And most unfortunately, we were standing in his way.

We stood face to face, not knowing what to do. Fred bent down slowly and picked up a stick that had broken off to a point.

"Our only chance is to scare him off."

"Let's not do anything that might make him mad," I whispered.

"We could turn and run," said Fred.

Sam inched backward. "That sounds good to me."

"But we'd probably get trampled from behind."

"That doesn't sound so good to me."

Fred eyed the huge, hairy ancestor of an elephant in front of us. He raised his stick and then threw it as hard as he could. The makeshift spear sailed through the air and struck the mammoth right between the eyes.

The mammoth blinked and slowly shook its gigantic head and pointy tusks. Fred's spear fell to the ground like a used toothpick. The mammoth lowered those pointy tusks in our direction and trumpeted.

"Time for another disappearing act," I said. "Because now I think you made him mad."

The hairy monster shook its mammoth head again and raised one mammoth foot.

And that's the last thing I saw because we turned and ran for the trees. We dodged around bushes and rocks. The mammoth smashed through the bushes and rocks. We were running as fast as we could, but the mammoth was still gaining on us and there was nowhere to hide.

We ran. Mammoth footsteps shook the ground behind us. We ran. Hot, smelly, mammoth breath blasted the back of my neck. I knew we were goners. But I wondered if our math teacher would believe the note from home: "Dear Mr. Dexter, Please excuse Joe, Sam, and Fred for not doing their math homework. They got run over by a woolly mammoth."

FROM **THE**

RIDDLE

by Susan Beth Pfeffer

illustrated by Tyrone Geter

STREAK

Just once, Amy would like to be better at something than her older brother Peter. He wins every game they play, and he seems to have an answer for every question. Out of desperation, she decides to become a riddle expert. After all, Peter can't know the answer to every riddle.

Amy sat next to Maria on the school bus Monday morning. "How many riddles does your grandfather know?" she asked.

"Millions," Maria said.

"I mean it," Amy said. "How many riddles?"

"I don't know," Maria said. "Lots and lots. Why?"

"Do you think he could teach me some?" Amy asked.

"Sure," Maria said. "Why do you need to know riddles?"

"To beat my big brother," Amy said.

"I wish I had a big brother," Maria said. "All I have are two little sisters. They drive me crazy."

"I'll trade you," Amy said. "One big brother for two little sisters and a grandfather who knows riddles. Do you think we could go visit him after school?"

"No," Maria said.

"Tomorrow then?" Amy asked. She didn't know how long she could wait before finding a riddle Peter didn't know.

"My grandparents went down to Florida this weekend," Maria said. "They won't be back until April."

"But that's months from now," Amy said. "I need a riddle right away."

"Try the library," Maria said. "Ms. Morris knows lots of good stuff."

Amy waited impatiently until the bus finally pulled into the school. As soon as she got off, she ran to the library. There were still a few minutes before the first bell was going to ring.

"Do you know any riddles?" she asked Ms. Morris.

"What kind of riddles?" Ms. Morris asked.

"Any kind," Amy said. "Hard ones."

"How many do you need?" Ms. Morris said.

"I don't know," Amy said. "I need a riddle my brother doesn't know."

"Oh dear," Ms. Morris said. "I remember Peter when he was at the primary school. He knew lots of riddles."

"Do you remember them all?" Amy asked. "If I know all the riddles he knows, then I could maybe find one he doesn't."

"Wait a second," Ms. Morris said. "I think there might be an easier approach."

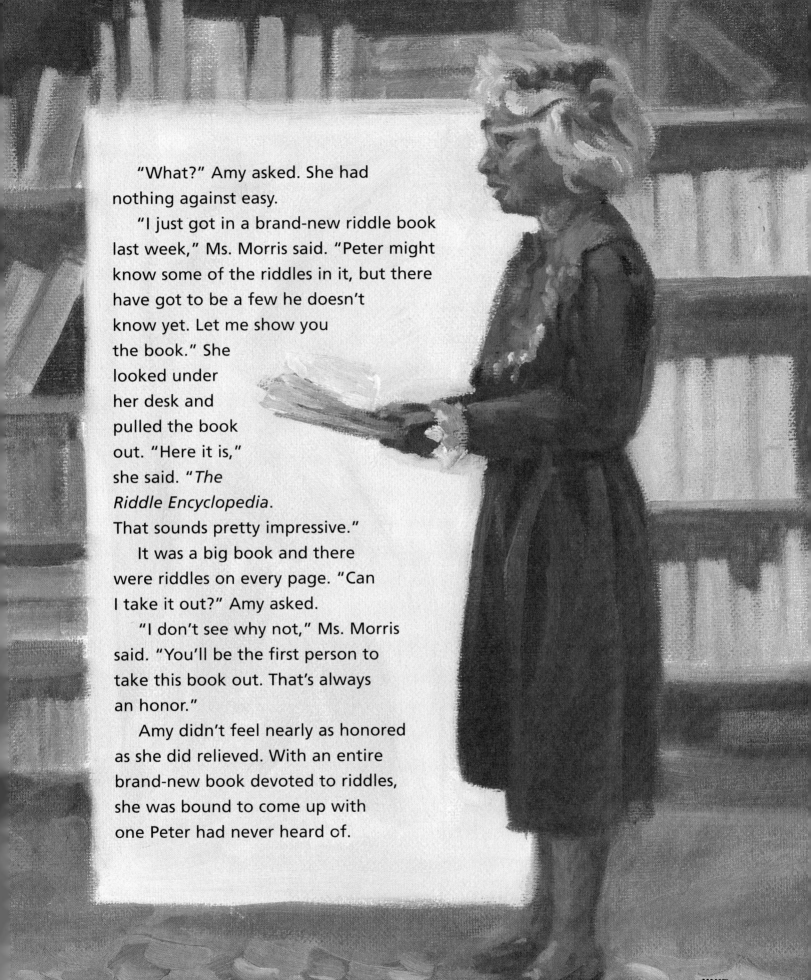

"What?" Amy asked. She had nothing against easy.

"I just got in a brand-new riddle book last week," Ms. Morris said. "Peter might know some of the riddles in it, but there have got to be a few he doesn't know yet. Let me show you the book." She looked under her desk and pulled the book out. "Here it is," she said. "*The Riddle Encyclopedia.* That sounds pretty impressive."

It was a big book and there were riddles on every page. "Can I take it out?" Amy asked.

"I don't see why not," Ms. Morris said. "You'll be the first person to take this book out. That's always an honor."

Amy didn't feel nearly as honored as she did relieved. With an entire brand-new book devoted to riddles, she was bound to come up with one Peter had never heard of.

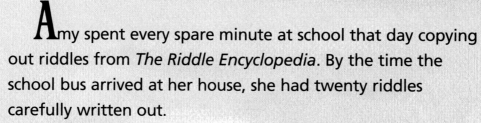

Amy spent every spare minute at school that day copying out riddles from *The Riddle Encyclopedia*. By the time the school bus arrived at her house, she had twenty riddles carefully written out.

It was wonderful picturing Peter not knowing the answers to any of them. She could see him stammer and stumble and finally cry as riddle after riddle went unanswered. Amy wanted a riddle streak of at least ten, but fifteen, or better still, twenty seemed really perfect to her. She'd earned her streak honestly, by going to the library and doing work. It had nothing to do with being older or bigger. Those kinds of streaks didn't mean anything.

She went crazy waiting for Peter to arrive home from school. Her mother was already there, but she was working in her home office, so Amy didn't feel she could interrupt. Besides, she'd certainly find out about it at suppertime, when Peter would still be crying.

Amy waited in the kitchen, writing out a couple more riddles. There was nothing wrong with a twenty-two riddle streak, or a twenty-five one. She wondered if Peter would ever stop sobbing. She kind of hoped not.

"I'm home!" Peter shouted when he finally got in.

"Mom's working," Amy said. "Don't shout."

"I'm home," Peter whispered instead, and then he laughed. Amy laughed too. It was probably the last time Peter would laugh in his lifetime. "Want some milk?" he asked Amy.

"I had some already," Amy said. She watched as Peter poured himself a glass. "Where do cars get the most flat tires?" she asked. She'd take him by surprise.

"At the fork in the road," Peter said. "Is there any cake left?"

"I don't know," Amy said. It was a good thing she had a few spare riddles to get her streak going. "There are cookies."

"Then I'll have them instead," Peter said.

"What goes out black and comes back white?" Amy asked.

"A cow in a snowstorm," Peter said. "No chocolate chip cookies, huh."

"Dad ate the last one yesterday," Amy said. "There are Fig Newtons left."

"I'd rather have chocolate chip," Peter said, but he took three Fig Newtons anyway.

"Why did the kid put his head on the piano?" Amy asked.

"Because he wanted to play by ear," Peter said. "Next?"

"What kind of doctor treats ducks?"

"A quack," Peter said.

Amy looked down at her list. Peter's riddle streak was definitely doing better than her own. It was a good thing she had a long list.

"What do brave soldiers eat?" she asked.

"Hero sandwiches," Peter said.

"What kind of cat works for the Red Cross?" Amy asked.

"A first-aid kit," Peter said. He rammed a Fig Newton into his mouth, then took a big gulp of milk.

"What pet is always found on the floor?" Amy asked.

"A carpet," Peter said. "Don't you know any hard ones?"

"I know lots of hard ones," Amy said. She searched her list frantically, looking for some hard ones. She was starting to feel really nervous. "What kind of house weighs the least?"

"A lighthouse," Peter said. He ate another of the Fig Newtons. "Are you sure there aren't any chocolate chip cookies left?"

"Why did the robber take a bath?" Amy asked.

"So he could make a clean getaway," Peter said. "What did you do, study riddles at school today?"

"I know lots of riddles you don't know," Amy said.

"Sure," Peter said. "And you can beat me in Ping-Pong any time you want."

"What travels around the world but stays in one corner?" Amy asked.

"A stamp," Peter said. "Do I get to ask you any riddles?"

"No," Amy said.

"That's a shame," Peter said. "Because I took out this really good riddle book from my library last week. It's called *The Riddle Encyclopedia*, and it had lots of riddles I never knew before."

"You already read *The Riddle Encyclopedia*?" Amy asked.

"Sure," Peter said. "My librarian showed it to me as soon as it came into the library. I read it on Saturday when you wouldn't play with me. Are you sure there aren't any chocolate chip cookies left?"

"I'm positive!" Amy shouted. She ran out of the kitchen and to her bedroom, leaving Peter behind with her list of foolproof riddles.

"**W**e're certainly quiet tonight," Mr. Gale said that evening as they finished supper. "Is there a reason why none of us is talking?"

"My mind's on work," Mrs. Gale admitted. "I'm sorry."

"I suppose your mind is on school," Mr. Gale said to Peter.

"No," Peter said. "I just don't have anything to say."

"What about you, Amy?" Mr. Gale asked. "Didn't anything interesting happen to you today?"

"No," Amy said. She certainly wasn't going to tell her father she'd spent the whole day learning riddles Peter already knew.

"In that case, how about dessert?" Mr. Gale asked. "I don't suppose there's any cake left?"

"We finished it last night," Mrs. Gale said.

"I was afraid of that," Mr. Gale said. "You know, I've been thinking about that cake all day long."

"It was good," Mrs. Gale said. "Sometimes I think cake-mix cakes are better than the ones you bake from scratch."

"What did the baseball say to the cake mix?" Amy asked.

"What?" Mr. Gale said.

"It's a riddle," Amy said. "What did the baseball say to the cake mix?"

"Nothing," Peter said. "Baseballs can't talk."

"They can in riddles," Amy said.

"This is a good riddle," Mrs. Gale said. "What did the baseball say to the cake mix? I don't know that one."

"Neither do I," Mr. Gale said. "How about it, Peter? You're the riddle king around here."

"Baseball," Peter said. "Cake mix. I don't remember that one from *The Riddle Encyclopedia*."

"Give up?" Amy asked.

"One more second," Peter said. "I must know it from somewhere. I know every riddle ever invented."

"I bet you don't know this one," Amy said. "Oh, I'm sorry, Mom, about betting."

"Don't be," her mother said. "I bet Peter doesn't know either."

"Do you, Peter?" Mr. Gale asked.

"I must," Peter said. "There can't be a riddle Amy knows and I don't."

"Your time is up," Mrs. Gale said. "I want to know the answer. Amy, what did the baseball say to the cake mix?"

"Batter up!" Amy said.

Everyone laughed. Except Peter.

"I never heard that one before," Peter said. "Where did you learn it?"

"I made it up," Amy said. "Just now, when Mom was talking about cake mixes."

"Did you really?" her father said. "I don't think I ever heard a brand-new riddle before. Peter, have you ever made up any riddles?"

"No," Peter said. "I never thought I needed to. There are millions of riddles already."

"Well, now there are millions and one," Mrs. Gale said. "Amy, that's wonderful, making up a riddle like that."

"I just thought of another one," Amy said. "Knock knock."

"Who's there?" Peter asked.

"Batter," Amy said.

"Batter who?" Peter asked.

"I'm batter than you are!" Amy sang in triumph.

Amy's parents laughed. "She got you on that one," Amy's father said to Peter.

"That's not fair!" Peter said.

"Why not?" his mother asked.

"I don't know," he admitted. "But it isn't."

"I have another one!" Amy said.

"You're kidding," her father said. "Amy, this is quite a riddle streak."

"What did Porky Pig say to the silverware?" Amy asked.

Her mother, father, and brother all stared at her. It was possibly the best moment in Amy's life.

"Th . . . th . . . th . . . that's all, forks!" Amy shouted.

Everyone, even Peter, laughed. "I've got to write these down," her father said. "I'll show them off at work tomorrow."

"Me too," Peter said.

"What do you mean?" Amy asked.

"Remember that guy, Mike Rudolph?" Peter asked. "The one who beats me in everything? He knows every riddle in the book. That's why I memorized them, to beat him at riddles, but it didn't work. Tomorrow I'll try Amy's riddles on him. He's bound not to know them. It'll drive him crazy."

"You'd better tell him they're mine," Amy said.

"I sure will," Peter said. "When he hears some dumb, I mean, smart little third grader made them up, he'll really go nuts."

"You want me to make up some more?" Amy asked.

"I sure do," Peter said. "After dessert, let's go to my room and I'll write them all down."

"Amy Gale, Riddle Champ!" her mother said. "Three brand-new riddles and still going strong."

It was definitely the best moment in Amy Gale's life.

WHO HAM I?

The Riddle King's Riddle Recipe!

By Mike Thaler
Illustrated by Jared Lee

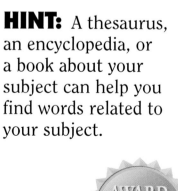

My name is Mike Thaler. They call me America's Riddle King! This is my riddle recipe. Use it to create millions of your own original riddles on any subject.

1. Pick a subject:

   PIG

2. Make a list of synonyms and related words:

   HOG, SWINE, OINK, HAM, MUD, SNOUT

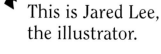

This is Jared Lee, the illustrator.

If you follow this simple recipe you can soon be a Riddle King or Riddle Queen!

So oinkers away! Have fun, happy riddling, and never forget: The most powerful nation in the world is your imagi-nation!

HINT: A thesaurus, an encyclopedia, or a book about your subject can help you find words related to your subject.

AWARD WINNING

Magazine

3. Take any word from the list: **HAM**
Drop off the first letter, leaving: **AM**

4. List words that begin with **AM**:
AMBULANCE, **AM**NESIA

5. Put the **H** back on:
HAMBULANCE, **HAM**NESIA

These are your riddle answers.

6. Now make up your riddle question using the answer's definition:

HOW DO YOU TAKE A PIG TO THE HOSPITAL?
Answer:
IN A HAMBULANCE

WHAT DO YOU CALL IT WHEN A PIG LOSES ITS MEMORY?
Answer:
HAMNESIA

HINT: In some cases, you have to drop off more than one letter to get a good word to work with. For example:

SNOUT – SN = OUT

OUTFIELDER + SN = SNOUTFIELDER
(What position does a pig play on a baseball team?)

OUTERSPACE + SN = SNOUTER SPACE
(Where do pig astronauts travel?)

How to Create a Comic Strip

With a *pen* and a *joke*, you can make your own *comic strip*.

What's the funniest part of the newspaper? Many people would answer, the comics. A comic strip is a story told with words and pictures. Some comic strips can be about serious subjects, even when they are funny. The words and pictures are in frames, and the last frame is the punch line—the thing that makes us laugh. Often the pictures make us laugh before we even get to the punch line.

1 Brainstorm Ideas

Come up with a list of funny ideas for your comic strip. Include jokes, stories, and funny things that have happened to you. Check your source materials for ideas. When you've finished your list, choose one idea to use for your comic strip. What makes your idea funny? Why does it make you laugh? Can you make a joke out of it? What kind of characters will you use to tell the joke?

TOOLS

- paper, pencil, and ruler
- colored pencils, markers
- joke books, magazines, comic strips

2 Plan Your Comic Strip

After you've picked an idea from your list, think about how to arrange your comic strip. Here are the steps.

Write the Dialogue: Write out the joke. Decide which character will say which lines. Then rewrite the joke using the fewest words possible.

Set Up Your Strip: Before you draw the final version of your strip, sketch out the words and pictures in a diagram like the one shown here. Write the words. Then sketch the characters into the frames. Next, draw speech balloons around the words. Be sure the reader can tell which character is speaking.

How Am I Doing?

Before you create your comic strip, take a few minutes to ask yourself these questions.

- Did I pick a funny joke or idea?
- Did I think about dialogue and pictures for my strip?
- What kind of characters will I draw?

PANEL 1 — The characters

PANEL 2 — Set up the joke.

PANEL 3 — Add to the joke.

PANEL 4 — Give the punch line.

3 Add Finishing Touches

Jazz up the joke. Next you're ready to create the final version of your comic strip. Look over the sketches and words on your strip. Do you think the joke is funny? Do the expressions on your characters' faces match their words? If you need to make changes, now is a good time.

Pictures make the joke seem funnier. Turn your sketches into really cool art. Use your art supplies and your imagination. Try making practice sketches with colored pencils and then with markers, to see which you prefer.

Create a background for your characters. Do your characters live in the woods? Are they standing on a city street? Think about what kind of background will help make your words even funnier.

- Use words like *zap* and *pow* to indicate sound effects.
- If you don't want to draw your characters, think about cutting out figures from magazines and newspapers.
- Use lots of bright colors.

4 Publish Your Comic Strip

When everyone's finished, put all the strips together to create giant newspaper "funny pages." Or you could bind the strips together to make a book. You could also submit your comic strip to the school newspaper.

CRASH

If You Are Using a Computer ...

Make a comic strip using your Card format. Begin your strip on the front, have one or two panels on the inside, and use the back for your punch line. Use the clip art, drawing tools, and speech balloons to make your strip look great.

CONGRATULATIONS

You've learned many ways that humor is used to make people laugh. Remember, a laugh a day is good for everyone.

Robb Armstrong
Cartoonist ▶

Glossary

an·i·mat·ed
(an′ə mā′tid) *adjective*
Having movement or
action, such as cartoon
characters. He saw the
animated version of *The
Three Little Pigs.*

art·work
(ärt′wûrk′) *noun*
Painting, drawing, or
sculpture. She showed
me her *artwork.*

bab·bling
(ba′ blĕng) *verb*
Making sounds that have
no meaning. The baby
started *babbling* in his
crib. ▲ **babble**

be·seech·ing·ly
(bi sēch′ ing lē) *adverb*
In a way that asks or
pleads for something. He
looked at his father
beseechingly.

boomed (bo͞omd) *verb*
Made a loud, deep
sound. His voice *boomed*
over the loudspeaker.
▲ **boom**

ca·reer (kə rēr′) *noun*
A profession or an
occupation that a person
has through life.
She chose social work as
a *career.*

car·toon char·ac·ters
(kär to͞on′ kar′ ik tərz)
noun
People or animals that
are humorously drawn.
▲ **cartoon character**

col·lage (kə läzh′) *noun*
A picture made by gluing
different kinds of
materials to a surface.

com·pet·i·tive
(kəm pet′ i tiv) *adjective*
Involving competition;
working against others
for the same prize or
goal. She was very
competitive, and wanted
to win the game.

Word History

The word **competitive**
comes from the Latin
word, *competere,* meaning
"to meet." A meeting
between athletes, such
as a sports event, is a
competition.

cre•a•tive
(krē ā′ tiv) *adjective*
Having and showing artistic abilities and imagination. His robot sculptures are very *creative*.

Thesaurus

creative
artistic
inventive
original

cried (krīd) *verb*
Called out in surprise.
▲ **cry**

dead•line
(ded′ līn) *noun*
The latest time by which something has to be completed. The *deadline* for handing in her report is Friday.

de•vel•op•ment
(di vel′ əp ment) *noun*
The act of creating something new. He worked on the *development* of a new product.

doo•dled
(do͞od′ ld) *verb*
Scribbled or drew things without paying attention. She *doodled* on the paper while talking on the phone. ▲ **doodle**

en•cy•clo•pe•di•a
(en sī′ klə pē′ dē ə)
noun
A book or set of books containing information arranged alphabetically on many different subjects.

fic•tion•al
(fik′ shə nl) *adjective*
Anything made up or imagined. The giant jackalope is a *fictional* animal.

fraz•zled
(fraz′ əld) *adjective*
To be emotionally or physically worn out. He looked old and *frazzled*.

a	add	o͝o	took	ə =
ā	ace	o͞o	pool	a in *above*
â	care	u	up	e in *sicken*
ä	palm	û	burn	i in *possible*
e	end	yo͞o	fuse	o in *melon*
ē	equal	oi	oil	u in *circus*
i	it	ou	pout	
ī	ice	ng	ring	
o	odd	th	thin	
ō	open	th	this	
ô	order	zh	vision	

Glossary

fron·tier
(frun tēr´) *noun*
The farthest settlement that lies next to an unexplored region. She had a hard life living on the *frontier*.

her·o·ine
(her´ ō in) *noun*
A woman admired for her bravery and courage. In the movie, the *heroine* saved the town.

hol·lered
(hol´ ərd) *verb*
Shouted or called loudly. He *hollered* for the dogs to come back. ▲ **holler**

il·lus·tra·tion
(il´ə strā´ shən) *noun*
A picture or diagram used to decorate or explain something. The poster *illustration* was beautiful.

im·ag·i·na·tion
(i maj´ ə nā´ shən) *noun*
The ability to form pictures in the mind; creative ability.

in·ci·dent
(in´ si dənt) *noun*
An event; something that happens. She described the funny *incident* to the class.

in·dig·nant·ly
(in dig´ nənt lē) *adverb*
In a way that expresses anger or scorn. The man spoke *indignantly* to the rude waiter.

me·di·a
(mē´ dē ə) *noun*
Materials used to create art. She tried many different *media* before deciding on oil paints.
▲ **medium**

mum·bling
(mum´ bling) *verb*
Speaking in such a low voice that the words are not understood. He was *mumbling* to himself.
▲ **mumble**

frontier

or·gan·ized
(ôr′ gə nīzd′) *adjective*
Arranged in an orderly way. She needed to be *organized* to do the experiment.

rep·u·ta·tion
(rep′ yə tā′ shən) *noun*
The character or quality of someone or something as judged by others. He had a *reputation* for being a good teacher.

Thesaurus

reputation
character
fame
status

re·sign·ed·ly
(ri zīn′əd lē) *adverb*
To accept something without really wanting to. When the bell rang, he *resignedly* handed in his test.

rid·dle (rid′ l) *noun*
A question or a problem that requires clever thinking to answer it.

self-dis·ci·plined
(self′ dis′ə plind) *adjective*
Controlling oneself. A writer needs to be *self-disciplined.*

shrieked (shrēkt) *verb*
Made a loud, shrill cry.
▲ **shriek**

slurp·ing
(slûrp′ ing) *verb*
Making a loud sipping sound; drinking noisily. The boy was *slurping* juice through his straw.
▲ **slurp**

speech·less
(spēch′ lis) *adjective*
Unable to speak for a moment. When he saw the present, he was *speechless.*

syn·o·nyms
(sin′ ə nimz) *noun*
Words that have similar meanings. Happy and glad are *synonyms* for cheerful. ▲ **synonym**

the·sau·rus
(thi sôr′ əs) *noun*
A dictionary of synonyms.

Word History

The word **thesaurus** comes from a Greek word that means "treasury." In the nineteenth century, it came to mean a book containing a treasury of words, specifically synonyms.

var·mint
(vär′ mənt) *noun*
A person or animal that is considered troublesome. The rat is a mean *varmint.*

Word History

Varmint comes from the word *vermin,* which is from the Latin word *vermis,* meaning "worm." Later, it came to be used for any unwanted animals, such as rats or fleas.

a	add	o͝o	took	ə =
ā	ace	o͞o	pool	a in *above*
â	care	u	up	e in *sicken*
ä	palm	û	burn	i in *possible*
e	end	yo͞o	fuse	o in *melon*
ē	equal	oi	oil	u in *circus*
i	it	ou	pout	
ī	ice	ng	ring	
o	odd	th	thin	
ō	open	th	this	
ô	order	zh	vision	

Authors & Illustrators

Judy Blume *pages 10–25*
Before starting a new book, this popular author fills a notebook with story details, including scraps of dialogue and other things she does not want to forget. Then she writes and rewrites. Most of her books take her more than a year to complete!

Tyrone Geter *pages 100–111*
Tyrone Geter has traveled to western Africa and has taught art at a university in Nigeria. Today he lives in Akron, Ohio, with his wife. He loves to illustrate books and is always busy with a new project. He also loves to teach. He divides his time between working on his own art and teaching art at the University of Akron.

Mary Pope Osborne *pages 72–81*

This author had a lot of jobs before she wrote her first book at age 30. She traveled around the world; worked as a window dresser, a waitress, and a medical assistant. But once she wrote a book, she finally knew what she really wanted to be: an author. Over the next 10 years, she wrote 20 books!

Tony Ross *pages 32–39*

The first drawings this illustrator created were cartoons for magazines. While trying to illustrate his first book for young readers, his editor told him the art was too stiff. The editor suggested he should draw the art like he drew his cartoons. Since then, Tony Ross has always had fun with his drawings.

Jon Scieszka *pages 94–99*

This author loves to have fun. His first book turned the well-known story about the Three Little Pigs upside-down: his version is told by the Big Bad Wolf! John Sciezka tests his story ideas on his own two kids, Casey and Jake, who make sure the stories are silly enough. They usually are! By the way, the author's last name is pronounced: sheh•ska.

"I get most of my ideas from hanging out with kids."

Books &

More by Jack Prelutsky

A. Nonny Mouse Writes Again
illustrated by Marjorie Priceman
Here are more poems by one of history's greatest poets.

The New Kid on the Block
illustrated by James Stevenson
This collection is full of poems about all kinds of humorous situations.

Tyrannosaurus Was a Beast
illustrated by Arnold Lobel
This collection of funny poems includes lots of facts about dinosaurs.

The Knee-High Man and Other Stories
by Julius Lester
This collection of folk tales comes from the African-American tradition. The tales are full of humor, trickery, and surprises.

Stage Fright
by Ann M. Martin
Sara Holland is the shyest girl in fourth grade. Now she has the leading role in the class play! This funny book tells about everything Sara goes through as she gets ready to be a star.

Wanted…Mud Blossom
by Betsy Byars
One of the funniest families in fiction searches for truth, justice, and their dog.

Funny You Should Ask
by Marvin Terban illustrated by John O'Brien
This book shows you how to create jokes and riddles by playing with words and their meanings. Get ready to make people laugh!

The Young Cartoonist: The ABCs of Cartooning
by Syd Hoff
This book is for kids who are just learning to draw cartoons. It has hundreds of illustrations, plus step-by-step instructions to help the beginner achieve results quickly.

&Media

Videos

Be a Cartoonist
Mid Com

Could you really draw your own cartoons? Professional cartoonist Alan Silberberg thinks so. He hosts this how-to video and explains the secrets of his craft. (60 minutes)

The Clown
Public Media Video

A homeless boy dreams of becoming a circus performer. One day he meets an old man who was once a clown. As their relationship grows and his respect for the elderly man increases, the boy finds a way to make his dream come true. (54 minutes)

Software

Cartoonin'.
Remarkable (IBM)

Create your own comic strip with the help of this program. It includes a drawing editor, story editor, and sound effects.

Print Shop Deluxe, Comic Characters Graphics
Broderbund (MAC)

This special add-on to a popular program gives you lots of graphics options to help you create your own comic strip.

Quicktoons
Wayzata (Macintosh with CD-ROM, IBM-Windows)

Enjoy classic cartoons on your computer with this resource.

Magazines

Cricket
Open Court

This magazine is full of all kinds of stories and articles. The cartoon adventures of Cricket and his friends run throughout each magazine, adding humor to every possible situation.

A Place to Write

Clowns of America, P.O. Box 570, Lake Jackson, TX 77566.

Clowns represent a classic form of comedy. Though it looks like a lot of fun, clowning around can be hard work. If you're interested in how to train to be a clown, you can write to Clowns of America.

NATURE
GUIDES

Enhydra lutris
SEA OTTER

Explore

a National Park

Gathering and using information help us understand and describe the natural world.

Nature Notes

We can observe and describe the natural world.

Wild Things

Writers create a picture of nature through their words.

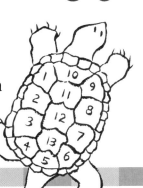

Take a Hike!

Each environment tells its own story about nature.

Trade Books

The following books accompany this *Nature Guides* SourceBook.

Newber

Classic Fiction

Charlotte's Web

by E.B. White
illustrated by
Garth Williams

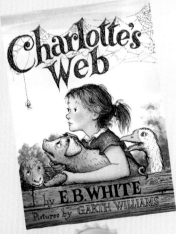

Nonfiction

Come Back, Salmon

by Molly Cone
photographed
by Sidnee
Wheelwright

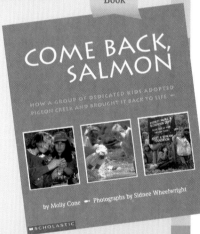

Biography

Listening to Crickets: A Story about Rachel Carson

by Candice F.
Ransom
illustrated by
Shelly O. Haas

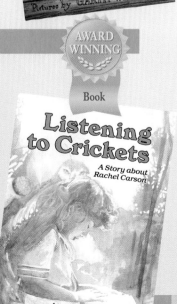

Fiction

The Secret of the Seal

by Deborah Davis
illustrated by
Judy Labrasca

Bison

Old Faithful

Larkspur

Elk refuge

Fawn

Nature Notes

Explore the swampy
Everglades through
the watchful eyes of
an alligator. Then get
the facts on this
endangered reptile.

Follow park ranger
Veronica Gonzales-
Vest on a nature trail
through an animal
sanctuary.

Hike through a
national park with
Ali Baba and keep a
lookout for bears.

WORKSHOP 1

In your nature log, record
observations of a favorite
outdoor place.

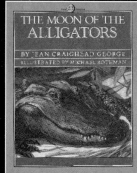

THE MOON OF THE
ALLIGATORS

BY JEAN CRAIGHEAD GEORGE
ILLUSTRATED BY MICHAEL ROTHMAN

Environmental
Fiction

FROM

THE MOON OF THE ALLIGATORS

By JEAN CRAIGHEAD GEORGE
Illustrated by MICHAEL ROTHMAN

Two eyes poked above the still water. Each iris was silver-yellow and each pupil black and narrow. They were the eyes of the alligator of Sawgrass Hole, who was floating like a log on the surface of the water as she watched for food. She saw the blue sky above her, and because her eyes were on the top and to the rear of her head, she saw all the way behind her to the tall cypress trees. Their limbs spread like silver wires above a tangle of sweet bay and buttonbushes.

The alligator did not move, but watched and waited even though hunger gnawed her belly.

She had eaten little since June, when the rainy season had flooded her home and the prey she fed upon had swum away. Now her sense of seasonal rhythm told her that the afternoon's cloudless sky meant the end of the rains and hurricanes, and the return of the wildlife to her water hole. The moon of October was the beginning of southern Florida's dry season. The water level would fall. The fish, frogs, turtles, and birds would come back to Sawgrass Hole, where she lived. They would be followed by the herons and ibis, egrets, anhinga or water turkeys, and she would eat well once more.

She was in her pool in the Everglades of Florida, which is not a swamp as it is often called, but a river like none other in the world. The Everglades does not flow—it seeps. Forty to sixty miles wide and a hundred miles long, it creeps, like glistening quick-silver, from Lake Okeechobee southward across a flat limestone bed to the Florida Bay. The Everglades is not only a river, but also a wet prairie. Saw grass, that rugged plant whose grasslike leaves are edged with sharp spines, grows like a crop from shore to shore. Rising out of the saw grass are tree islands, known as hammocks, where a variety of trees grow. Other islands are forests of bay, called "heads," buttonwood and cypress trees.

The Everglades and its plants and creatures, including the alligator, have adapted to the wet and dry seasons of the semitropical zone in south Florida. When the river is high in summer's wet season, little fish, like guppies and gambusia that eat mosquito larvae, swim among the saw grass stalks far out in the river. They dodge the largemouth bass and sunfish, who, in turn, avoid the Florida soft-shelled turtle.

During the winter season when the river is low, the wildlife of the Everglades adjusts to dryness. As the water level drops, and just before the river bottom becomes exposed to the sun and cracks, the river creatures come to the alligator holes. They live through the drought of winter in these watery sanctuaries.

October was always a critical time for the alligators as they waited for their food to return. In this century, however, the month of October has become a near disaster for them. Human-made canals, dug into the limestone to drain the Everglades for farming, have killed off millions and billions of frogs, fish, birds, mammals, and turtles. Their food depleted, the alligators died in huge numbers from starvation. In addition, hunters killed tens of thousands for their valuable skins. The passing of the alligators threatened all the wildlife in the Everglades, for their holes are oases for life during the dry season. The great flocks of beautiful birds were reduced to a few. Fish and turtles died out for lack of winter retreats. The alligator, people began to realize, was the "farmer" that kept the chain of life going.

In the 1970s there were so few American alligators left on this earth that Congress declared it an endangered species, one that is doomed to extinction and would be protected by law. Since that decree, the big reptiles have made a strong comeback in their original homeland that stretches from Texas to North Carolina. They are now only a threatened species.

The six-foot alligator of Sawgrass Hole did not know about her status, she only knew her belly ached. Sinking to the bottom of the pool, she looked for food. The river was getting low. A few minnows too small to bother with darted past her. A measly pollywog rested in the warm mud.

She ignored it, whipped her tail from side to side, and then circled her large home. The water was filling with algae, one-celled plants that grow profusely in the sun. Long strips of these green plants floated in scummy masses. They bothered her.

With a powerful thrust from her tail she drove her body into a patch of algae and caught it on her nose. Swimming with surprising grace, she carried it to the shore and pushed it up with her nose and feet, then returned and bulldozed another load ashore. Next she went to the overgrown water lilies floating on the surface. Taking a plant in her mouth, she tugged it across the pool and dragged it up on land to die.

When she was done she could see the minnows more clearly, and the minnows, freed from the weeds, flickered back and forth across Sawgrass Hole eating microscopic food called periphyton. In the days that followed, they grew rapidly and larger fish fed on them. For the alligator, however, there was no food big enough for her to bother with.

Her hole, which was fifteen feet deep and some forty feet long and wide, was far out in the Everglades at the edge of a cypress head. On one of its shores was a beach where she sunbathed. Around the edges of the pool in the shallow water grew pickerelweed and arrow-heads. Among their stems the fry of the largemouth bass grew up. On the shore, just out of the water, grew clumps of six-foot-tall alligator flags. Their large leaves, on the ends of long stalks, waved and fluttered like banners. These plants announce the locations of alligator homes to human, bird, and beast. When the big reptiles are killed or die, the plants die too, for there is no alligator-farmer to weed. The algae multiply and clog the pools, weeds take over the shallows and shore and, finally, trees and bushes fill in the pond, choking out the alligator flags.

One evening the big 'gator lay near the shore watching the bushes. The moon of October was working its change. The water in the river was lowering, and the fish and wildlife were coming to her deep hole. A snowy egret alighted on a limb of a pop ash near the water. The bird no longer held his feathers close to his body as he did in summer, but lifted them slightly to let his delicate plumes float down the back of his neck like a veil. The moon of October is the beginning of the breeding season for the egrets. In a month or so he would strut for his mate, spread his plumes, then bow and dance for her.

The egret picked up a stick, held it a moment, then dropped it. It was a present for his mate, but he was not quite ready to give it to her. October was a time to practice the art of courtship, and practice he did. He picked up another stick. The alligator eyed him but did not stalk. He was too high in the tree to catch.

The bird flew, his yellow feet and black legs gleaming as he skimmed over Sawgrass Hole and climbed into the air. High over the 'gator hole, he turned and headed for his rookery on a buttonwood island near the Florida Bay. The 'gator watched him until he was out of sight, then submerged herself in the river. She made no ripples to alarm her prey, nor did she disturb the waters as she pressed her huge jaws together. They closed over seventy sharp white teeth, forming the perpetual grin of an alligator. Her tail, almost half of her length, torpedoed her across the pool to the shore where the cypress trees grew. As she came up on land, water spilled from her sculptured armor and her third eyelid pulled back to let her see in the air.

The alligator saw movement beneath a pop ash. Rising to her feet on short legs, she peered into a brushy jungle that she and her ancestors had created. For a thousand years the alligators of Sawgrass Hole had made land by weeding and piling the debris on this shore. Tree seeds had rooted in the rich compost. The seedlings had grown into a sheltering jungle that attracted rabbits, raccoons, bobcats, and river otter.

The 'gator lunged at a marsh rabbit who was nibbling on leaves. He had been born in late summer. With the rise of the moon of October he had left home to seek his fortune. He had not gone far before he came upon the alligator's jungle and, finding it rich with rabbit food,

settled in. Blackish-brown in color, he looked like the cotton-tail rabbits of the north, except that he had no white on his tail. However, he did possess their ability to leap, and before the alligator could lunge a second time, he had catapulted over her tail and plunged into the pool. He swam quickly across Sawgrass Hole and bounced ashore. Marsh rabbits are excellent swimmers.

Being so close to catching a rabbit made the alligator even hungrier. She dove into her pool and scanned the undersides of the bladderworts, floating plants that catch insects and take nourishment from them. No dark areas marked the bodies of resting frogs. They were still out in the glades. Patiently she waited.

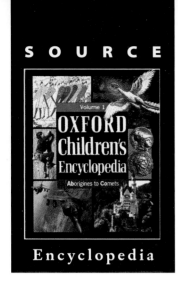
ALLIGATORS

Alligators

Alligators and their close relatives the caymans are short-snouted members of the crocodile family. True alligators seem to be able to survive in colder conditions than their relatives. They live further north and may hibernate during the winter.

Most species of cayman and alligator probably live and develop in much the same way as the much-studied American alligator. All species swim well and feed from the water on fish and mammals, and they all lay their eggs in sand. The Chinese alligator spends much time in a burrow dug into a river bank.

The skin of alligators and caymans makes valuable leather, and many have been destroyed because of this. In some cases the disappearance of these animals has led to ecological disaster, as the insects, rodents and fish on which they feed have increased in number and become pests. ■

from OXFORD CHILDREN'S ENCYCLOPEDIA

Chinese alligator

American crocodile

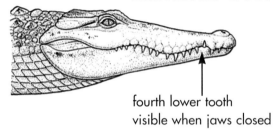

fourth lower tooth
visible when jaws closed

▲ Alligators have shorter, blunter snouts than crocodiles. When a crocodile's mouth is closed, the large tooth fourth from the center on the lower jaw still shows near the front of the mouth and fits into a notch in the upper jaw. No lower teeth can be seen when an alligator shuts its mouth.

DISTRIBUTION

The American alligator is found in the warm parts of the southern United States and as far north as North Carolina. The Chinese alligator lives by the lower Chang Jiang (Yangtze) River. Caymans live in tropical parts of Central and South America.

LARGEST about 5.8 m

NUMBER OF EGGS 25–55

LIFESPAN 56 years in captivity

SUBPHYLUM Vertebrata

CLASS Reptilia

ORDER Crocodilia

NUMBER OF SPECIES
Alligators 2, caymans 5

The American alligator is likely to be seen by visitors to the Florida Everglades in the USA. At one time it was very rare, but because of conservation its numbers have now increased.

◄ Alligators spend much time basking in the sun or lying in wait for their prey. They swim by moving their long, powerful tails from side to side.

Veronica Gonzales-Vest

Park Ranger

Park rangers see some wild things!

Park ranger Veronica Gonzales-Vest works at the Sequoia National Park in California, which is famous for its giant trees. Sequoia trees are the largest living things in the world. Gonzales-Vest loves her job. She spends her days outdoors, patrolling the park and taking visitors on nature hikes.

PROFILE

Name: Veronica Gonzales-Vest

Occupation: national park ranger

What every park ranger needs: a flashlight

Favorite animal: acorn woodpecker, because of the rat-a-tat sound it makes

Significant park memory: brought snow from the park to a school where the kids had never touched or smelled snow before

Favorite vacation spot: Santa Fe, New Mexico, where she grew up

QUESTIONS

for Veronica Gonzales-Vest

Here's how one park ranger *manages* information *about* nature.

Q **How did you learn all the information about nature that you share with park visitors?**

A I learned by observing the wildlife in the park, and talking to other park rangers. I also read lots of reference books. That's why, when I take people on nature hikes, I can tell them about the plants and animals they'll see. And I warn them not to wander off. It's not part of the park experience to become lunch for a bear!

Q **Do you use special tools to observe nature?**

A The tools I use are my eyes, ears, nose, hands, and brain. I use my senses—listening for birds, smelling wildflowers, and so on.

Q **How do park rangers tell how old a sequoia tree is?**

A Park rangers are skilled at "reading the rings." They take a core sample from the tree and then count the rings from the center out. One light-colored ring plus one dark ring equals one year's growth. Sequoias can live to be 3,200 years old!

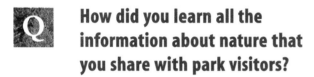

Pocket Guide to Songbirds

A Field Guide to Butterflies

North American WILD FLOWERS

 Why do you think your job as a park ranger is important?

 There isn't anywhere else like Sequoia National Park. I love telling people about the park. I see kids' eyes light up when they learn new nature facts. Some of them may decide to become park rangers!

 What are some popular sites at Sequoia National Park?

 The Tunnel Log is a popular attraction. It was made from the trunk of a sequoia and is wide enough to drive a car through. After a visit to the tunnel, people can say they've driven through a tree. Another favorite site is the General Sherman tree. This tree is probably over 2,000 years old. (Imagine a cake with that many candles!) It's also *very* large. One of its branches is over 140 feet long!

Veronica Gonzales-Vest's Tips for Young Naturalists

1 Use all your senses when observing nature.

2 Move quietly to avoid scaring the animals. You'll see more.

3 Be prepared. Carry a notebook and binoculars on your nature walks.

27

from
Ali Baba Bernstein, Lost and Found

AWARD
WINNING

Author

Ali Baba
Hunts for a Bear

by Johanna Hurwitz
illustrated by Michele Noiset

The summer after Ali Baba's tenth birthday, he and his parents went on a trip to Wyoming. When Mr. Bernstein first announced to his son that they were going to vacation in a couple of parks, Ali Baba thought he was making a joke.

The Bernsteins' apartment in New York City was near two parks—Riverside Park and Central Park. Both were nice places. When he was little, Ali Baba had played in the sandbox or on the swings and slides in the parks. It was good to have trees and grass in the middle of the city. But how could you take a vacation in the park?

"These parks are different," Mr. Bernstein explained to his son. "National parks are huge, and people come from all over the country to visit them."

"People come from all over the world," Ali Baba's mother added.

Ali Baba was sure they were exaggerating.

On the day that Ali Baba Bernstein was ten years, two months, and seven days old, they arrived in Grand Teton National Park in Wyoming. Then he saw that his parents had not been exaggerating at all. The park was huge. In fact, it looked bigger than Riverside Park and Central Park and a hundred other parks combined. And just as his parents had said, it was filled with thousands and thousands of tourists.

Some were Americans like Ali Baba. He began noticing the license plates on the cars. In the first hour in the park, he spotted plates from Illinois, Colorado, California, and Wyoming. The car that Mr. Bernstein had rented had license plates from Minnesota. When they stopped for lunch, a man came over to them.

"Whereabouts in Minnesota do you live?" he asked.

"We live in New York," said Mr. Bernstein, explaining about the rented car.

"I was born in St. Paul, Minnesota," said the man. "I thought you might come from there, too."

Ali Baba and his parents were staying in a little log cabin. In the parking lot near the cabins, there were three huge buses. The men and women coming out of the buses looked just like Americans, but Ali Baba couldn't understand a single word they said.

"What are they saying?" he asked his parents.

"I don't know," said Mrs. Bernstein. "They are speaking German." Because she didn't know the language, she could only guess what the people were talking about.

What most people seemed to be talking about were the animals. The park was filled with them. At home, the only animals Ali Baba ever saw in the park were squirrels and dogs. The dogs were supposed to be kept on leashes, but they often ran loose.

Here, there were herds of buffalo and antelope and deer. Sometimes you could see them very close to the road. Other times they were off in the distance.

Mr. Bernstein had brought a pair of binoculars, and Ali Baba kept busy searching for animals. He thought he would ask his father if he could borrow the binoculars when he got home. They seemed like very useful equipment for a would-be detective.

"I saw a bear," a girl told Ali Baba proudly as he was adjusting the binoculars at a lookout point the first morning.

"Where?" asked Ali Baba. He wondered if the girl was telling the truth. He hadn't seen any bears.

"Not here," said the girl. "When we were driving in Yellowstone National Park."

"Was it big?" asked Ali Baba.

"Huge," said the girl.

It seemed as if everything in the park was huge.

"Maybe I'll see a bear, too," said Ali Baba, putting the binoculars to his eyes.

"You probably won't," said the girl. "It's very hard to see them nowadays. My father said that when he came here twenty years ago, there were lots of bears."

"If you saw one, then I'll see one," said Ali Baba with certainty. He was determined to see a bear before he went back to New York City.

After that, Ali Baba spent all his time searching for a bear.

Mr. Bernstein took loads of pictures. He made Ali Baba smile into the camera at least a dozen times a day. Ali Baba found that very boring. It was embarrassing, too, if there were other people around. Most of the time, however, the other people were so busy posing and taking their own pictures that they didn't even notice.

"I see a bear!" Ali Baba shouted that afternoon.

"Where? Where?" asked his mother, looking around.

Mr. Bernstein grabbed his camera, ready to focus it at the elusive animal.

"Ha-ha! I made you look!" Ali Baba laughed. He had really fooled his parents.

"Do you remember the story of the boy who called wolf?" asked Mr. Bernstein. "If you try and trick us now, no one will believe you if you ever do see a real bear."

So Ali Baba kept watch for a bear. And he began to keep score of the animals he did see:

moose	17	marmot	1
buffalo	39	antelope	8
beavers	3	deer	12
gophers	61	coyote	1

He didn't bother to count mosquitoes. They had mosquitoes at home.

There were many things to do in the park. One morning,
they got up extra early and took a ride on a rubber raft on
the Snake River. Everyone, even Ali Baba who had passed his
intermediate swimming test the summer before, had to wear
bright orange life vests. It was very quiet out on the water.
The splashing of the oars made the only sound. The guide
told them to listen carefully. Soon they could hear the sounds
of birds calling and animals grazing near the water.

"I see a bear!" Ali Baba called out. The hair stood up on
his arms, and his heart began beating rapidly. It was an
exciting moment, but it lasted only a second.

What Ali Baba saw wasn't a bear at all. It was a large
tree stump. "I really thought it was a bear," Ali Baba

protested. He hadn't been trying to fool anyone this time. He felt silly making a mistake like that. The other people on the raft all laughed.

"It's pretty hard to find a bear around here these days," said the guide. "That stump is just the color of a bear. No wonder you got confused." Ali Baba knew he was saying that to make him feel better, but he didn't. He hadn't seen a bear, and he had been careless enough to mistake a tree stump for an animal. A good detective wouldn't do that.

"Is that a bear?" asked Mr. Bernstein a little later. Everyone on the raft turned to look. But it was the back end of a moose half hidden by a bush. Ali Baba smiled at his father. It was nice to see that other people made mistakes.

That afternoon, the family went horseback riding. Mr. Bernstein was the only one in the family who had ever ridden a horse before. Mrs. Bernstein was very nervous. Ali Baba felt a little scared himself, but he would never admit it. He wondered what would happen if a bear approached. Would it frighten his horse? Would he fall off?

"Are there any bears around here?" he asked the man in charge of the horses.

"If there were, the horses would smell them long before we could spot them," said the man. "The bears like to be left alone. They don't come where there are so many people and other animals."

So Ali Baba spent the next hour concentrating on riding and not on bears. It was a lot of fun, and he couldn't wait to go home and brag to Roger about his newest accomplishment. Still, even though he was having such a good time, Ali Baba wished he would see a bear before he went home. Perhaps he would have better luck at Yellowstone National Park, he thought as they drove to the second park.

Just as before, whenever they were driving along and they saw a group of parked cars, Mr. Bernstein would pull off along the side of the road, too. Parked cars usually meant that someone had spotted animals in the area. Ali Baba kept watching for a bear.

"Is there a bear?" Ali Baba always wanted to know.

"I saw a bear yesterday," said a boy who appeared to be a year or two older than Ali Baba.

"So did I," said Ali Baba. He was about to add that the bear he had seen turned out to be only a stump of an old tree. However, the older boy interrupted him.

"Hey, that's neat," the boy said, smiling at Ali Baba.

"It's getting really hard to see a bear around here these days. There're just a few of us who have done it. You must have good eyes, like me."

Ali Baba felt trapped. There was no way he could change his statement now.

"Aaaah, yeah," he mumbled.

"Where do you come from?" the boy asked.

"St. Paul, Minnesota," said Ali Baba. The words just flew out of his mouth even though they weren't true.

"I'm from Worthington, Ohio," the boy said. "My name's Greg. What's yours?"

Having already told two lies, even if one was not intentional, there was no way Ali Baba was going to identify himself. He couldn't even say his name was David, which was vague enough, as there were so many Davids in the United States.

"Larry," he said. The name just popped into his head. Ali Baba didn't know anyone named Larry, and he didn't know why he picked that name.

Luckily, at that moment, Greg's parents called him to get back into their car. They were ready to drive on.

"See you around," said Greg.

"Yeah," said Ali Baba, hoping that they would never meet again.

That evening at supper, there was a family with two small boys sitting at the next table in the park cafeteria.

"You know what?" one of them said to Ali Baba.

"What?"

"There's a kid around here named Barry, and he saw a bear."

"Really?" asked Ali Baba. He didn't feel he had to impress these two boys. And besides, he still felt uncomfortable about the story he made up to tell Greg.

"Yeah. He comes from St. Charles. That's in Missouri near where we live."

That made two guys who had seen bears, Greg and Barry. Ali Baba wished he had been that lucky.

The next day, Ali Baba sat eating an ice-cream cone when he was approached by a little girl of about five or six.

"Did you see any bears?" asked the girl.

"No," said Ali Baba. "Did you?"

"No. But there must be one around, 'cause some boy named Harry saw two of them."

"Really? How do you know?" asked Ali Baba.

"Some kids told me. Harry came here from St. Matthews. That's in Kentucky where I live."

Ali Baba licked his ice-cream cone thoughtfully. Either there were a lot more bears around than he had thought, or else there were no bears at all. It was a curious coincidence that Harry and Barry both came from cities that started with the word *Saint*. In fact, when he thought of it, so did Larry, the fellow he had invented. Larry came from St. Paul. Ali Baba was sure he was onto something now.

Ali Baba walked over to his father. Mr. Bernstein was comparing cameras with another man. A young girl stood beside the man, and she looked at Ali Baba. "Have you seen any bears?" he asked her.

The girl shook her head. "No," she said. "But I heard about another girl named Mary, just like me, and she saw a bear."

"I bet she lives in St. Paul or St. Matthews or somewhere like that," guessed Ali Baba.

"I don't know where she lives," said the Mary who stood along side of him.

Ali Baba started counting on his fingers: Larry, Barry, Harry, Mary. . . . He wondered how many other names there were that rhymed: Jerry, Carrie, Gary, Terry. He bet there were dozens of cities that sounded alike, too.

So when Ali Baba was ten years, two months, and seventeen days old, he returned home from a trip to Wyoming without having seen a single bear. However, he had solved a mystery that no one but he even knew existed. He had seen how a single accidental lapse from the truth had grown into a group of kids and a bunch of bears.

It was something to bear in mind for the future.

How to
Keep a Nature Log

Observations are as detailed as possible.

Naturalists and nature lovers can spend hours observing wildlife. They make sketches and take notes about what they are observing. They keep this information in a nature log.

What is a nature log? A nature log is a record of someone's observations of living things. Each entry describes plants and animals found in one place at one time. A log contains notes, pictures, diagrams, and rubbings.

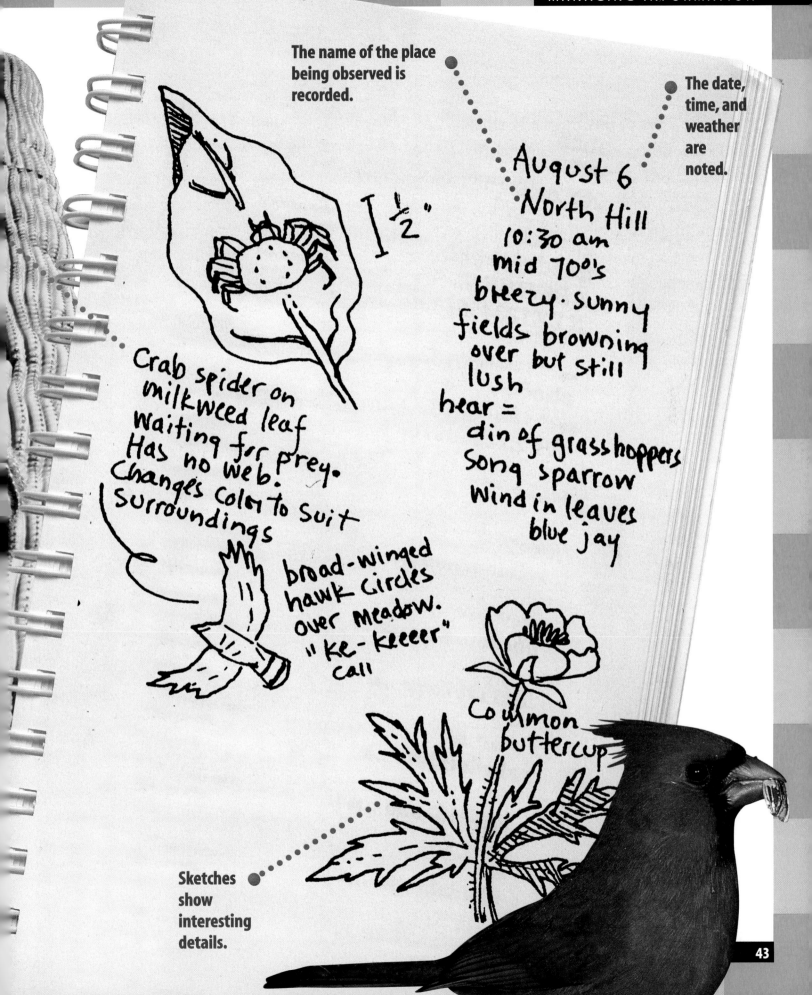

The name of the place being observed is recorded.

The date, time, and weather are noted.

$I \frac{1}{2}"$

August 6
North Hill
10:30 am
mid 70°'s
breezy. sunny
fields browning
over but still
lush
hear =
din of grasshoppers
song sparrow
wind in leaves
blue jay

Crab spider on
milkweed leaf
waiting for prey.
Has no web!
Changes color to suit
surroundings

broad-winged
hawk circles
over meadow.
"Ke-keeeer"
call

Common
buttercup

Sketches show interesting details.

1 Brainstorm

Make a list of nearby places where you can observe animals and plants. What about a corner of your school grounds, a park, or your backyard? A patch of grass along the sidewalk can be home to many small creatures, including insects. Choose the place that will be easiest for you to visit and observe.

TOOLS

- pencil and notebook
- protective clothing
- magnifying glass
- reference books about animals and plants

2 Make a Nature Log Page

- Write the name of your observation site at the top of a notebook page.

- Label the page: "Date," "Time," and "Weather." Be sure to leave plenty of space for jotting down details and making drawings.

3 Observe and Record

Visit your site, and observe the living things around you for at least 20 minutes. Take notes and make sketches. Record any questions you have about what you see. When you leave, your log entry should be full of information and have at least two sketches.

Tips
- **Remember not to pick anything that's growing.**
- **Be quiet. Many animals, including birds, will hide unless you keep still.**
- **Use your eyes, ears, and nose.**

4 Do Research

What questions did you write in your log? What were the most fascinating plants or animals you observed? Find out more about them in encyclopedias and field guides. Write down the five most interesting facts you learned from your research. Then share your log and research with your class.

If You Are Using a Computer ...

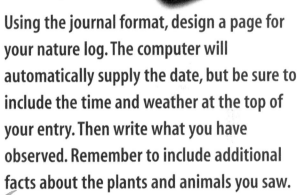

Using the journal format, design a page for your nature log. The computer will automatically supply the date, but be sure to include the time and weather at the top of your entry. Then write what you have observed. Remember to include additional facts about the plants and animals you saw.

THINK

Imagine that you are an ant on a blade of grass. What kinds of things would you see through the eyes of an ant?

Veronica Gonzales-Vest
Park Ranger ▶

Hermit crab

Brown pelican

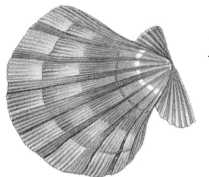

Lion's paw

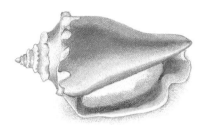

Florida fighting conch

Hibiscus

Writers create a picture of nature through their words.

Wild Things

Join a young naturalist as she observes the wildlife of the Galápagos Islands.

Discover how a turtle's shell can be used as a calendar.

Read a humorous folk tale and find out how the leopard got its spots.

WORKSHOP 2

Make a diagram of a living thing you see in its natural environment.

from

Swimming
with SEA LIONS
and Other Adventures in the Galápagos Islands

by Ann McGovern

The Galápagos Islands are 600 miles west of the mainland of Ecuador, South America. There are fifteen large islands and about forty small islands. Some of the small ones are just rocks jutting out of the Pacific Ocean.

Day One
First day in the Galápagos!!!
San Cristóbal Island

Dear Diary,

    I can't believe that Grandma and I have already spent almost a whole day in the Galápagos Islands. Everything is like a strange dream.

    Today I walked right up to birds and they didn't fly away! Grandma talked to sea lions—and they talked back with funny barks and burps. I've never seen such tame wild creatures in my whole life!

    Living on a boat is strange, too. Our boat is called the *Mistral.* Grandma and I share a small cabin. There's a tiny bathroom in our cabin.

It's funny to think of sleeping and eating and going to the bathroom on a boat for two weeks.

The Galápagos has been a dream trip of Grandma's for years. I'm so lucky she asked me to come along.

I think I'll start from the beginning. There was snow on the ground when Grandma and I left New York. After three different plane rides, we came to these hot islands on the equator, in the Pacific Ocean!

When we landed at the little airport, we were met by Andy, our guide. I found out that every boat that travels around the Galápagos Islands has a licensed guide who knows everything about these islands and the creatures who fly, crawl, and swim here.

Grandma is keeping a diary of Andy's facts for me to add to *my* diary. I'm going to put her pages at the end. This is the symbol I'll use to show that there's more information in Grandma's diary. ✺

The *Mistral*—my home for two weeks. There were eight other passengers and four crew members.

Grandma and the other scuba divers look happy after a dive.

Andy says we'll spend most of our days on shore walking around the islands, looking at the creatures—mostly birds and reptiles. I asked him about swimming, my favorite sport. He said sometimes we'll swim from a beach, and sometimes we'll jump off the boat into the water.

A few people plan to scuba dive, including Grandma! She says she wants to dive with fish that are found only here. And she wants to look at hammerhead sharks, huge manta rays, and sea turtles.

I was on the ship for only an hour when I saw my first flying fish skimming just above the water.

Still Day One Later

Dear Diary,

We are anchored close to land. Dozens of sea lions doze and sun on the shore. Others play in the water.

I jumped off the boat and got a big surprise. Even though it's broiling hot in the middle of the day, the waters of the Galápagos Islands feel real cold.

Grandma snorkeled with me. We peered down into the sea through our clear face masks. We use snorkel tubes for breathing, and the fins on our feet make it easy to swim.

I saw yellow-tailed surgeonfish beneath me—there must have been a hundred of them!

Suddenly a big body—then another—bolted past us. Grandma and I were quickly surrounded by *ten* adorable young sea lions!

It was a circus in the sea! Sea lion pups dived beneath us, blowing silvery bubbles through their noses. They somersaulted and flipped themselves into pretzel shapes. They chased and nipped each other. They are like big kittens. They seemed to be showing off just for us. They never scared me.

But the big male sea lion on shore did scare me with his bellowing roar! The other sea lions answered the bull with barks and coughing and burping sounds. It sounded like they were going to throw up.

Andy told us that the bull sea lions try to keep other males away. They also keep watch for sharks.

Sea lions live on almost every island so I will be seeing a lot of them. I'm glad because so far they are my most favorite creatures. ❋

I took this shot of a playful sea lion pup with an underwater camera. Isn't she adorable?

Andy didn't mind when this finch flew up and pulled out a strand of his hair. I never saw anything like that before! Andy said the bird just wanted the hair for its nest.

Still later

Tonight I saw my first Galápagos sunset. The sky was glowing, and the sun was setting over a big rock that rose out of the sea.

Day Two
Santa Cruz

Dear Diary,

This morning we anchored in Academy Bay off Santa Cruz, one of the four islands in the Galápagos where people live.

I'm so excited! After lunch I'm going to see giant Galápagos tortoises—the largest land tortoises in the world! At the Charles Darwin Research Station I'll get to see them up really close. Grandma says the station was named for Charles Darwin, who sailed to the Galápagos in 1835 on the ship the *Beagle* and later became a famous scientist.

I just found out that *galápagos* means tortoise in old Spanish.

This tortoise is hiding in its shell. Maybe I scared it. (I didn't mean to.)

Later

Dear Diary,

I am so mad I could cry!

I read up on giant tortoises before lunch. Once there were hundreds of thousands of these huge tortoises on the Galápagos Islands.

Long ago, explorers, pirates, and seal and whale hunters came here. They stayed at sea for many months, and sometimes years. The fresh meat of the giant tortoises kept them from starving to death. The sailors knew that tortoises can stay alive for a year without food or water, so they stacked them by the hundreds in the damp, dark holds of their ships, one on top of another. Oh, those poor creatures.

Rats are no friends of tortoises, either. There were never rats here until the ships brought them. The rats swam to shore and began to destroy tortoise eggs and young tortoises. Rats are still around today. No wonder there are so few giant tortoises left.

The good news is that today there's hope for the tortoises. Andy told me that thanks to the Charles Darwin Research Station and the National Park Service, a lot of giant tortoises are being saved. ✾

Before bedtime

Dear Diary,

I saw them! I couldn't believe my eyes! I had read that giant tortoises can weigh over 500 pounds so I wasn't expecting a little box turtle. But I never dreamed there could be such big tortoises. And they looked so old with their great wrinkled necks and teary eyes.

At the Research Station the bigger tortoises are kept outdoors in large fenced areas, and the younger ones are in indoor pens.

My favorite tortoise is Lonesome George. Once he lived on Pinta Island with thousands of other tortoises. Hunters came to Pinta and took all the tortoises they could find. But somehow they missed one tortoise.

In 1973, workers from the Darwin Station came to Pinta Island to get rid of the wild goats that were destroying so much of the plants. The workers discovered the one tortoise that was left behind. Since he was the only one of his species left, they named him Lonesome George and brought him back to the station.

Grandma and Marty, one of the passengers, are surrounded by giant tortoises on Santa Cruz Island.

Spooky *scalesia* trees grow only in the Galápagos.

In the middle of the night

Dear Diary,

I can't stop worrying about tortoises. They're still in danger. Besides the goats that eat the plants and the grasses that are the tortoises' food, there are cats, dogs, pigs, rats, and donkeys that roam the islands and destroy tortoise eggs and baby tortoise hatchlings.

When I grow up, I want to work at the Charles Darwin Research Station and help save the baby tortoises.

Day Three
Santa Cruz

Dear Diary,

What a day! I talked Grandma into letting me go with Andy and a few others to look for giant tortoises in the highlands.

Andy told me to wear a scarf around my neck, but it was such a hot day that I stuck it in my pocket.

We got on a rickety old bus and started our climb into the highlands. Pretty soon we were in an evergreen forest. We got out and hiked the rest of the way. The woods smelled good, like spices, but it was spooky. Strange moss hung from the branches of twisted trees.

And talk about mud! Sometimes I was almost up to my knees in muddy goo. We seemed to walk for hours—then I saw my first tortoise in the wild! I was so excited I began to shout.

I guess I shouted too loud because right away its head and feet disappeared into its shell, or *carapace* as Andy calls it. And that carapace was all any of us saw of any tortoise the whole day!

On the way back, I was feeling bad about scaring the tortoise when suddenly I felt a stinging bite on my neck. Then another, and another, till my neck felt like it was on fire!

I began to dance around like crazy. Andy ran over to me and rubbed some cooling lotion on my neck.

He told me I was being bitten by fire ants that drop from trees. If I had worn my scarf around my neck like he had told me to, they wouldn't have been able to attack me.

I squeezed my eyes shut to keep from crying. First, I scared the only tortoise we saw. Second, it was my own stupid fault that I got bitten by fire ants. And third, Andy is mad at me.

Dear Diary, you know what? I'm sorry I ever came to the Galápagos.

A giant tortoise like this can live for over 100 years.

Later

Dear Diary,

Andy's not mad at me after all! He came up on deck of the *Mistral* where I was watching the sunset. Together we watched the sky glow and quickly turn night-black. He told me a story about a special expedition he had gone on to see the giant tortoises on Isabela Island.

With a group of people, he had hiked up to the top of the volcano where everything grows lush green and where the fog swirls so thick and wet that it drips water. The thousands of tortoises that live there aren't shy, like the Santa Cruz tortoises.

They didn't even seem to care that people were around. They just kept on munching plants.

When the tents were set up, the tortoises plodded up to inspect them. They sniffed the gear, too, and stepped on it and began to chew on it! The people had to build a fence of logs to keep the curious tortoises out of camp.

Then, Andy said, it started to pour. Dozens of tortoises came to drink the rainwater that collected in pools. Andy said it was magical.

The way he talked, I could picture the whole expedition.

I love Galápagos tortoises more than anything.

A Galápagos sky just as the sun is setting—a sight I will never forget.

More About the Galápagos

Here are a lot more facts that Grandma kept for me in her diary.

❋ **Day One**
More About Sea Lions, page 52
Sea lions live in groups. One big male bull takes charge of a family of about forty females and their young. Andy says these sea lions are closely related to the California sea lions.

❋ **Day Two, Santa Cruz**
More About Charles Darwin, page 53
Charles Darwin was a young British naturalist whose job on a round-the-world voyage on the *Beagle* was to collect and study plants and animals.

❋ **Charles Darwin Research Station, page 54**
In 1959, the Charles Darwin Foundation was formed to protect the unusual life on the Galápagos. Scientists from all over the world come to study the plants and animals.

The Charles Darwin Research Station sends workers to different islands to collect tortoise eggs. They bring the eggs back to the station where they are protected until they hatch. Thousands of hatchlings have been raised at the station. The little tortoises are cared for until they are five years old, old enough to have a good chance of surviving in the wild. Then the tortoises are returned to their own islands where eventually they mate and produce young tortoises.

The creatures of the Galápagos are protected by rules made by the Charles Darwin Research Station and the Galápagos National Park Service.

All the guides make sure the rules are followed. Touching or feeding any of the creatures, wandering off the marked trails, or taking anything—even a broken shell or a piece of lava—is against the rules.

from

Thirteen Moons on Turtle's Back

A NATIVE AMERICAN YEAR OF MOONS

by Joseph Bruchac and Jonathan London
illustrated by Thomas Locker

Grandfather leaned over the long spruce log. The small boy stood close, waiting for the old man to notice him.

Grandfather looked up, a small smile on his face.

"*Kway*, Sozap," he said, "you do well at watching. Come closer. See now what I have done."

Sozap reached up to touch the carved shape of Turtle.

"How many scales are on Old Turtle's back?" Grandfather said. "*Kina* look."

Sozap counted with care.

"Thirteen," he answered.

"*Unh-hunh!*" Grandfather said, "There are always thirteen on Old Turtle's back and there are always thirteen moons in each year. Many people do not know this. They do not know, as we Abenaki know, that each moon has its own name and every moon has its own stories. I learned those stories from my grandfather. Someday, Grandson, if your memory is as sharp as your eyes, you will be able to tell them to your grandchildren."

"Grandfather," Sozap said, "do other Native people have moons, too?"

The old man nodded. "Yes, Grandson."

Moon
of Popping Trees

Outside the lodge,
the night air is bitter cold.
Now the Frost Giant walks
with his club in his hand.
When he strikes the trunks
of the cottonwood trees
we hear them crack
beneath the blow.
The people hide inside
when they hear that sound.

But Coyote, the wise one,
learned the giant's
magic song,
and when Coyote sang it,
the Frost Giant slept.

Now when the cottonwoods
crack with frost again
our children know, unless
they hear Coyote's song,
they must stay inside,
where the fire is bright
and buffalo robes
keep us warm.

FIRST MOON
Northern Cheyenne

62

Budding Moon

One year Old Man Winter
refused to leave our land,
and so our people asked for help
from our great friend, Ju-ske-ha,
known to some as the Sun.
He knocked on the door
of Winter's lodge
then entered and sat
by Winter's cold fire.

"Leave here or you will freeze,"
Winter said,
but Ju-ske-ha breathed
and Winter grew smaller.
Ju-ske-ha waved his hand
and a white owl flew down
to carry Winter
back to the deep snow
of the north.

The lodge melted away
and the trees turned green
with new buds
as the birds began to sing.
And where the cold fire
of winter had been
was a circle of white May flowers.
So it happens each spring
when the Budding Moon comes.
All the animals wake
and we follow them
across our wide, beautiful land.

FIFTH MOON
Huron

64

Strawberry Moon

In late spring
a small boy
whose parents had died
went hunting game
down by the river
where the Jo-ge-oh,
the Little People who care
for the plants, live.

He shared what he caught
with those Little People.
In return they took him
in a magic canoe
up into the cliffs,
taught him many things
and gave him strawberries.

He was gone just four days,
but when he returned
years had passed
and he was a tall man.
He shared with his people
what he was taught and
gave them the sweetness
of the red strawberries.
So, each year, the Senecas
sing songs of praise
to the Little People,
thanking them again
for this moon's gift.

SIXTH MOON
Seneca

Moon of Falling Leaves

Long ago, the trees were told
they must stay awake
seven days and nights,
but only the cedar,
the pine and the spruce
stayed awake until
that seventh night.
The reward they were given
was to always be green,
while all the other trees
must shed their leaves.

So, each autumn, the leaves
of the sleeping trees fall.
They cover the floor
of our woodlands with colors
as bright as the flowers
that come with the spring.
The leaves return the strength
of one more year's growth
to the earth.

This journey
the leaves are taking
is part of that great circle
which holds us all close to the earth.

TENTH MOON
Cherokee

Turtle's Calendar

Thirteen Moons

1) Moon of Popping Trees

2) Baby Bear Moon

3) Maple Sugar Moon

4) Frog Moon

5) Budding Moon

6) Strawberry Moon

7) Moon When Acorns Appear

8) Moon of Wild Rice

9) Moose-Calling Moon

10) Moon of Falling Leaves

11) Moon When Deer Drop Their Horns

12) Moon When Wolves Run Together

13) Big Moon

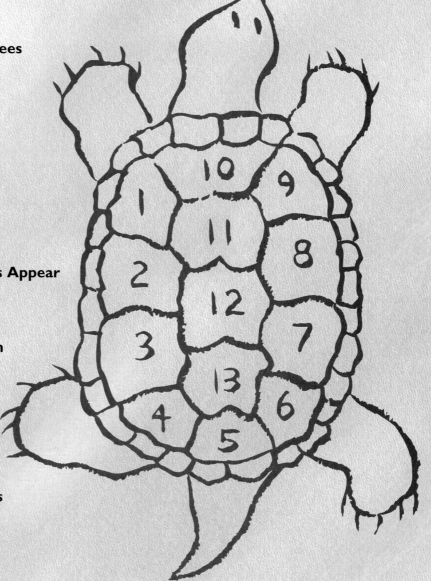

Authors' Note

The native people of North America have always depended upon the natural world for their survival. Watching the changes going on in the natural world with each season, they also look up into the sky and see it changing. In many parts of North America, the native people relate the cycles for the moon (called Grandmother Moon by many Native Americans) to those seasons. In every year, there are thirteen of those moon cycles, each with twenty-eight days from one new moon to the next.

Many Native American people look at Turtle's back as a sort of calendar, with its pattern of thirteen large scales standing for the thirteen moons in each year. As Grandfather says to Sozap and as an Abenaki elder said to me long ago, it reminds us that all things are connected and we must try to live in balance.

J.B. and J.L.

SOURCE

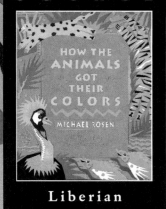

Liberian
Folk Tale

AWARD
WINNING

Author

FROM

HOW THE ANIMALS GOT THEIR COLORS

Retold by **MICHAEL ROSEN**
Illustrated by **JOHN CLEMENTSON**

LEOPARD

See Leopard. He can leap so quick he's out of sight before you've blinked. Watch him.

See Nyomo. His eyes are so good, he can stand at the bottom of a tree and see a fly on the topmost leaf. Watch him.

You've heard of Lion? Wait for him. He comes later.

One day Leopard says to Nyomo, "Let's go, you and me, and find wild honey."

They walk, Leopard's paws pad on the ground. *Foop, foop, foop.* Nyomo's feet glide beside Leopard. *Shoo, shoo, shoo.*

"Look there!" says Leopard. "A bees' nest. I am the first to see a nest full of honey!"

They look inside. "No honey," says Nyomo. "Walk on."

They walk. *Foop, foop, foop* go Leopard's paws. *Shoo, shoo, shoo* go Nyomo's feet.

"Look there!" says Nyomo. "A bees' nest. I am the first to see a nest full of honey!"

They look inside. "Honey!" says Nyomo. "Let's eat."

They eat honey until their bellies are full and their eyes go wild. "Leopard," says Nyomo, "give yourself a name. What name do you want to call yourself?"

"Strongman," says Leopard. "And you?"

"I'm Ironman," says Nyomo. "And Ironman is a better name than Strongman."

Leopard growls, Leopard snarls, Leopard rages at that. He grabs Nyomo, ties a rope around his middle, and drags him through the forest. They meet Barking-deer.

"Say, Leopard, don't you know better than to go dragging Lion's brother along like that?" asks Barking-deer.

"I know what I know," says Leopard. "You just mind your own business, Barking-deer."

"Say, Nyomo," says Barking-deer, "will you tell me what's going on?"

"I said Ironman was a better name than Strongman, and Ironman is the name I'm going to have."

Barking-deer laughs. He laughs and laughs until it hurts. "You? Nyomo? Ironman? Little Nyomo who can't lift a log, can't bite a bone, can't even fight a fly—you call yourself Ironman in front of Leopard? You deserve everything you get."

Leopard is thinking: *Nyomo is Lion's brother. So I'll take him to Lion, and he'll tell Nyomo who's who around here.* Leopard drags Nyomo to Lion. When Lion sees his brother tied up, he is furious. Lion tells Leopard right there what to do.

"Set Nyomo free," says Lion. Leopard sets Nyomo free.

"Fetch water," says Lion. Leopard fetches water.

"Fill the bath," says Lion. Leopard fills the bath.

"Nyomo, my brother, bathe yourself in the clear, cool water." Nyomo climbs into the bath.

"Leopard, get under the bath. Stay there." Leopard gets under the bath.

Nyomo's hot, dry, dusty skin softens and shines in the bath, but the dirty water dribbles over Leopard. Leopard growls. "*Rrrr, rrrr, rrrr.*"

Now Nyomo rests. Lion and his wife bring food and sit and eat with Nyomo. They eat and eat and eat until all that's left is bits of bones, peels, and husks.

"Nyomo, dear brother," says Lion, pointing to the scraps. "Why not take these delicious little tidbits to Leopard?"

Nyomo takes bits of bones, peels, and husks to Leopard. This drives Leopard into a roaring rage.

"Lion," roars Leopard, "I'll tear you into so many pieces, it'll take ten years to count the bits."

Lion doesn't move.

"Lion, I'll throw you so high, you won't come down until next year."

Lion doesn't move.

"Lion, I'll squash you so flat, you'll blow away on the wind like a leaf."

Lion moves. Lion rises. Lion pounces on Leopard; Leopard fights back. Biting, clawing, raging. Every piece Leopard bites out of Lion, he swallows. Every piece Lion bites out of Leopard he drops on the ground.

Then, see who's coming—Old Mother. She comes near. She sees Lion and Leopard locked together, fighting in the hot dust. She sees Lion tearing at Leopard. "Run Leopard!" she cries, "Run Leopard, before Lion kills you!"

So Leopard runs. He runs and runs until he finds a pool of cool mud. With his paws, he picks up clumps of mud, and, *fap, fap, fap,* he pats them into the holes Lion made. *Fap, fap, fap,* he closes them over until there are no holes left. Then Leopard lies down to get better.

Everything's fine for Leopard now, but his skin stays spotty forever.

How to Draw a Wildlife Diagram

A picture of a plant or animal provides a certain amount of information. A wildlife diagram provides more detailed information. That's why wildlife diagrams are often used to illustrate field guides and references books.

What is a wildlife diagram? A wildlife diagram is a detailed sketch of a plant or an animal. Like all diagrams, each part of the subject is identified with a label. A wildlife diagram also includes interesting facts about the plant or animal. These facts usually give information about the subject's habitat or feeding habits. Looking at a wildlife diagram is a quick way to get a lot of information!

Horse Chestnut Twig

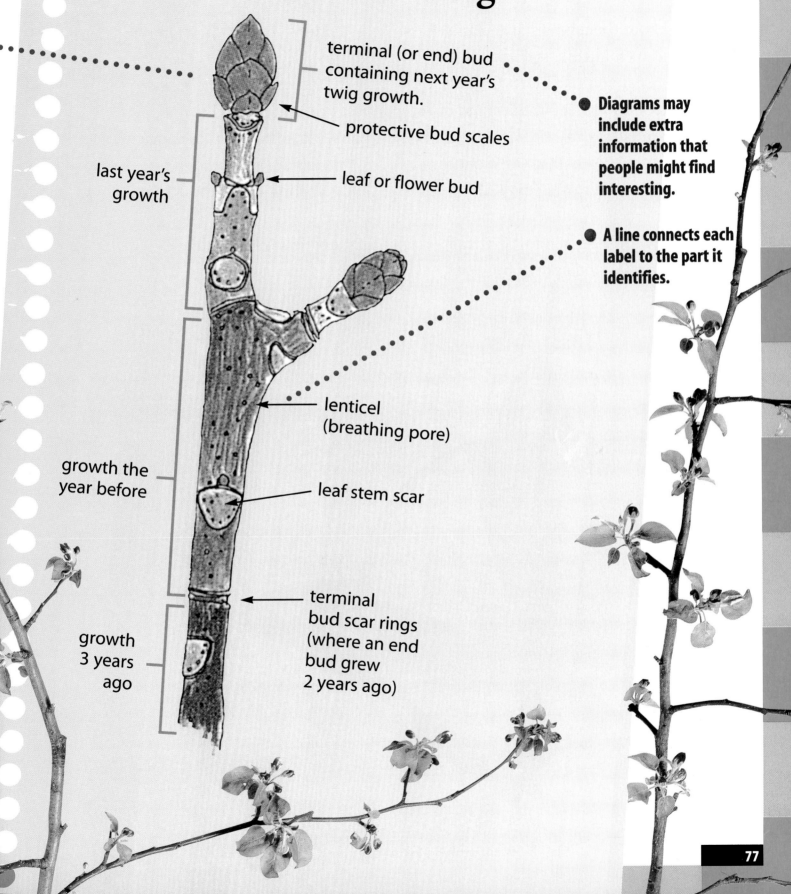

terminal (or end) bud containing next year's twig growth.

protective bud scales

leaf or flower bud

last year's growth

lenticel (breathing pore)

growth the year before

leaf stem scar

terminal bud scar rings (where an end bud grew 2 years ago)

growth 3 years ago

Diagrams may include extra information that people might find interesting.

A line connects each label to the part it identifies.

1 Choose an Animal or a Plant

Think about the animals and plants you've seen. Is there a specific kind of bird or insect you like? Do you have a favorite kind of tree? Make a list of your favorite animals and plants. Then decide on one that you want to learn about. You may wish to pick something that can be easily observed up close.

TOOLS

- pencil
- ruler
- construction paper
- field guide or encylopedia
- colored markers

2 Make a Diagram

Carefully observe the plant or animal you've selected, and draw a picture of it. You can also find a picture of it that you can trace. Then label its parts. Look through an encyclopedia, a field guide, or a nature book for help with labeling the parts. Use more than one resource to get information. Have fun with your diagram. Make it colorful by using markers.

Tips
- Trace a magazine photo if you are having trouble making an accurate sketch.
- Check an encyclopedia or a field guide for examples of diagrams.

3 Investigate Further

During your research you'll probably learn some interesting facts about the animal or plant you've chosen. How long does it live? What kinds of food does it need? Does it have any enemies? Decide on three "fascinating facts" to add to your diagram. Write them on the bottom of the page.

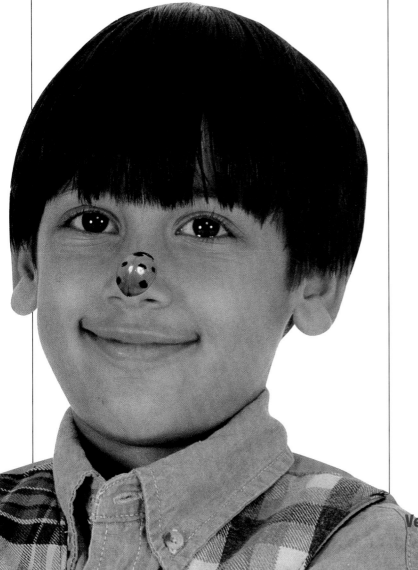

4 Classify the Diagrams

When everyone has finished, put all the diagrams together. Divide the class projects into two groups: animals and plants. For example, a diagram of a ladybug would be put in the same group as a diagram of a turtle. The class may want to turn these groupings into books.

If You Are Using a Computer ...

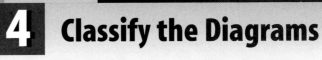

Type and print out the title of your diagram and labels, using different fonts. Add clip art to illustrate the facts on the bottom of your diagram.

THINK

How can a diagram help a naturalist tell the difference between plants or animals that look alike?

Veronica Gonzales-Vest
Park Ranger ▶

Morpho butterfly

Three-toed Sloth

Passion flower

Giant armadillo

Scarlet macaw

Amazonia lily

Each environment tells
its own story about nature.

Take a Hike!

Visit a suburban
backyard and
discover the
wildlife that
thrives there.

Take a walk with
a nature watcher
who shares his
secrets for
tracking and
observing animals.

Join a young boy in
his exciting search
for a black fox.

PROJECT

Create a field guide about
the animals and plants in an
outdoor place.

My
Field
Guide

81

from
The City Kid's Field Guide
by Ethan Herberman

In Your Own Backyard

Do you know what's going on in your backyard?

A homeowner near Scranton, Pennsylvania, certainly thought he did. So when he found a man with earphones wandering around his property, he refused to believe the trespasser's excuse. The man said he was Gary Alt, a wildlife biologist for the Pennsylvania Game Commission, and that a 400-pound (180-kg) black bear tagged with a radio transmitter was living in the homeowner's hollow tree. "You're crazy!" said the homeowner. "So," says Alt, "I took a big stick, gave the tree a whump, and out popped the bear at the top.

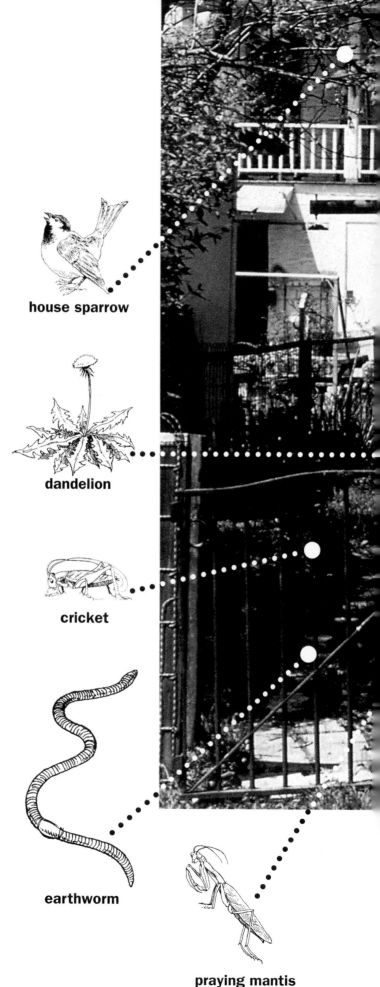

house sparrow

dandelion

cricket

earthworm

praying mantis

raccoon

What lives in our backyards? Just the plants we put there and the animals we seek to attract? Or are there raccoons in the garbage? Rats amid the hibiscus bushes? Dandelions ducking the mower on the lawn? Quite possibly. For all species, whether they appeal to you or not, have certain basic requirements—food, water, space in which to reproduce and take cover—and these a backyard often provides.

Few black bears take advantage of the food and shelter available in human communities. But in Pennsylvania, some do and the average "backyard bear" is about 200 pounds (90 kg) heavier than its wild counterpart.

The homeowner took off. It took a long time to convince him that the bear was only there to hibernate, that it wouldn't hurt his kids."

Backyards, of course, are supposed to be private places. We plant tulips here, maples there, juniper by the fence. However, the environment we create in this way suits more than just these "invited" species. Perhaps you have heard the motto of many a self-made millionaire. "I saw my opportunities and I took 'em," they like to say— which is, as it happens, the strategy of successful living things everywhere. They find their opportunities, and they take 'em. Cottontail rabbits find your vegetable patch, dandelions your fertile lawn....

Only rarely, of course, do bears find dens in the suburbs. Even without them, however, you can turn up much that is fun and unexpected in your backyard.

It's Green, with Eyes like a Space Alien

You wouldn't want to be a caterpillar in the flower bed when a praying mantis shows up.

You might want to be a plant, since the arrival of the mantis with its huge appetite would likely spell the end of your Japanese beetle problem—not to mention your grasshopper problem, your earwig problem....

But probably the best thing to be in relation to a praying mantis is a human being. Merely seeing an insect of its size will amaze you. It may be three inches (7.5 cm) long, so large that you can make out all the details: the triangular head, the huge round eyes, the raised-up body, the spiky forelegs.

Piece by piece, a praying mantis eats a garden spider, a fearsome hunter that was still no match for the mantis's jagged claws.

Praying mantises lay grape-sized egg cases all over town—on lawn furniture and buildings, as well as on plants. Move one to your yard, and some 200 baby mantises will soon be gobbling down everything they can grab, including each other.

These the giant holds as if in prayer, giving it its name. But it's not praying. It's hungry. Praying mantises always seem to be hungry. Watch one hunt and you are unlikely to forget the meaning of the word "predator" again.

You won't see it chase things around, though. For the most part, the mantis will do little more than wait until the motion of a nearby insect attracts its attention. Then the head swivels about, much as your head does. Sometimes the body sways, ever so slowly, in the direction of the hapless prey nearby. It may be a small insect, like a fly. On the other hand, it may be a bumblebee. But no matter. In a flash the mantis's forelegs have sprung out. Faster than your eyes can follow, the mantis has grasped its quivering victim in those jagged claws—and its former slowness returns. The victim, after all, will never escape, and the mantis has no interest in gobbling it down. Instead, it raises the insect to its mouth and bites off a piece. Finishing that one, it bites off some more.

Does it seem strange that people would buy creatures like these for their gardens? Well, think it over. Which would you prefer to remove your insect pests: mantises or a deadly insecticide spray?

The spray will work for a time. It will clear the garden of most plant-destroying insects. But a few of the pests may have a natural resistance to the poison spray. When these individuals breed, they will pass their immunity on to their young. A new population of insects that can resist the poison will grow, and before long your plants will be as infested as before.

Using insects to control each other is a safe and long-lasting way to protect your yard.

Temperature (in °F) = number of chirps in 15 seconds + 40!

Natural Thermometers

When people start paying attention to nature, they are sometimes surprised at how much it has been telling them all along.

Take heat and cold. Many plants and animals react noticeably to changes in temperature. The rhododendron is a fine example. As the winter temperature sinks, rhododendron leaves curl down, closing up tighter and tighter to protect themselves. Keep watch on the position of those leaves when you know the temperature, and you'll soon be able to read them when you don't.

To find out how warm it is, however, you need no experience at all. Simply listen for the group singing of snowy tree crickets. You'll know you're listening to snowy tree crickets when you hear about two chirps every second. Since warmer crickets sing slightly faster than colder ones, if you count the number of cricket chirps in fifteen seconds, then add forty, you will get the approximate temperature in degrees Fahrenheit. Say you hear thirty-eight chirps in fifteen seconds. Thirty eight plus forty is seventy-eight: It's seventy-eight degrees out.

Crickets sing by rubbing their front wings together. Only male crickets do so, however. Their purpose: to attract a mate.

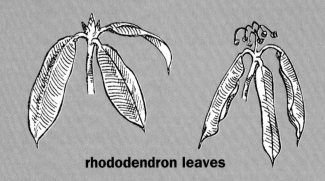

rhododendron leaves

To convert Fahrenheit to Centigrade: subtract 32, multiply by 5, divide by 9.

Every can is a treasure. A mother raccoon and her cubs dig into someone's garbage. Notice their furry "masks," powerful bodies, and banded tails. About the only items they won't eat are raw onions.

Impawssible

"But that's impossible," you might say as you pick up the trash strewn all over the yard. "I sealed those cans firmly last night."

Any number of night roamers might have done it: skunks, squirrels, dogs, even your neighbor's cat. But if you really pressed those lids down tight, latched the box, even weighed it down with a heavy rock, then the chances are that the mess was caused by a raccoon.

And chances are it'll be back to do it again tonight.

People seem to have tried everything in their war with these large-brained animals. They've latched chicken coops, and the raccoons unlatched them; they've sealed up doorways, and the raccoons came in through the chimney; they've hung sacks of bird food on strings from trees, and the raccoons untied—didn't chew through, *untied*—the string.

Despite efforts to deter them, raccoon numbers are booming: More of them wander through some North American communities than ever prowled the same regions before the cities were built. One study turned up 150 per square mile (2.6 square km) in an Ohio suburb. They're fat, too, as you have probably seen.

To understand the raccoon's success, follow the next one you see waddling through mud or snow. Don't come too near—don't ever approach or corner a raccoon because it may carry rabies and may bite you. Instead, examine the tracks it leaves behind. Don't the forepaws look like a small child's hands? They are about that sensitive, and what's more, the raccoon is ready to take full advantage of whatever gets within its grasp.

It eats just about everything that comes its way—everything meaning berries, frogs, fish, beetles, breakfast cereal, even kittens. Like the cockroach, it has adapted well to the buildings of humans. In the wild, raccoon nests are often found in hollow trees; but in the city they have been found in sewers, culverts, garages and attics, not to mention the ventilation systems of buildings downtown.

How do raccoons pry off lids and untie string? With sensitive front paws that look much like a child's hands and leave similar imprints in mud and snow.

child's hand

raccoon's forepaw

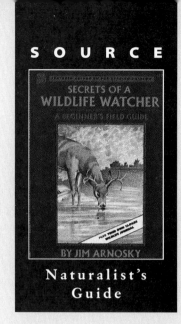

from

SECRETS OF A WILDLIFE WATCHER

by

JIM ARNOSKY

AWARD WINNING

Author

It was the first cold morning of winter. The ground was hard and coated with frost. I stepped briskly, following a deer path that skirted an open field. A deer had just been walking on the path. Its hoofprints were dark marks melted in the white frost. A sudden gust of bitterly cold wind whipped across the field, stinging my face. I pulled my coat collar up over my cheeks and nose. Just then I saw the deer!

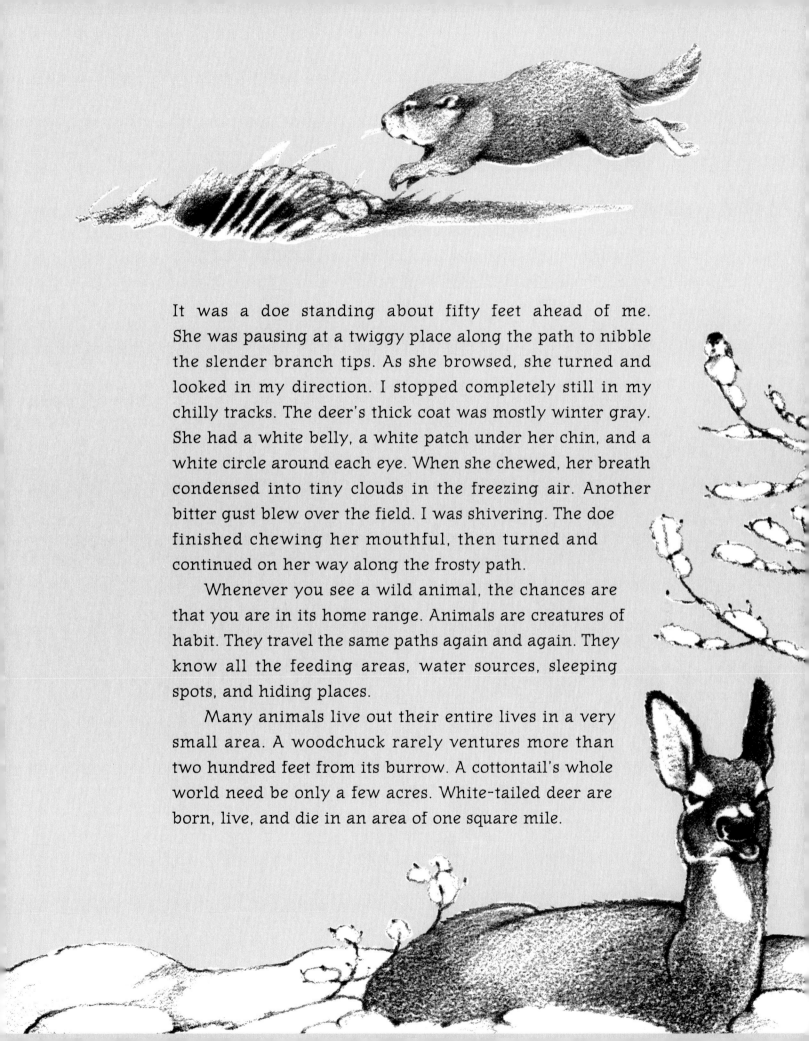

It was a doe standing about fifty feet ahead of me. She was pausing at a twiggy place along the path to nibble the slender branch tips. As she browsed, she turned and looked in my direction. I stopped completely still in my chilly tracks. The deer's thick coat was mostly winter gray. She had a white belly, a white patch under her chin, and a white circle around each eye. When she chewed, her breath condensed into tiny clouds in the freezing air. Another bitter gust blew over the field. I was shivering. The doe finished chewing her mouthful, then turned and continued on her way along the frosty path.

Whenever you see a wild animal, the chances are that you are in its home range. Animals are creatures of habit. They travel the same paths again and again. They know all the feeding areas, water sources, sleeping spots, and hiding places.

Many animals live out their entire lives in a very small area. A woodchuck rarely ventures more than two hundred feet from its burrow. A cottontail's whole world need be only a few acres. White-tailed deer are born, live, and die in an area of one square mile.

Different animals can have overlapping ranges. On one short hike in a wrinkle of a mountain, I found fresh tracks of fox, coyote, weasel, bobcat, and bear. All are predators. They are natural enemies, competing for available food. I'm sure they avoided meeting one another, but their tracks crossed, paralleled, and often followed the same trails.

A predator's home range is a hunting territory that it prowls over and over. A fox's hunting territory may cover one mile; a coyote's two or three miles. A river otter's hunting territory can stretch to twenty miles around. It takes the otter about twelve days to complete the circuit. If you remember where you have seen an animal once, you will eventually be able to see it there again.

Last summer a trio of otters included the pond behind my house in their hunting territory. Every two weeks I kept an eye on the pond, expecting them to show up. They always did. From a hiding place on the bank I watched them roll and twist acrobatically in the water. When one would dive out of sight, I would find it again by watching the line its breath bubbles made on the surface. Often the diver's wet head popped out of the water with a

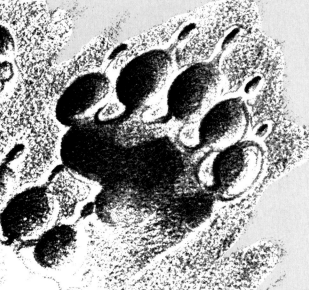

TRACKS OF BLACK BEAR
AND COYOTE I FOUND
PRESSED SIDE BY SIDE
IN THE MUD NEAR
A MOUNTAIN SPRING

gleaming trout clamped in its mouth. The otters always took trout in their front paws and ate them like candy bars, head to tail, in big, crunchy bites. Whenever they noticed me, all three would duck under water and vamoose.

Look for wildlife where water meets land, field meets wood, or lawn meets hedge. On these open "edges" sunlight stimulates a variety of plant growth that animals can eat while remaining near the safety of cover. This is why you often see animals along the roadside. They are attracted to the edges created by the road swath. The biggest white-tailed deer I've ever seen was standing on a roadside. It was a deep-bodied buck with eight long points on its antlers.

The wide ribbons of sunlit, brush-covered land on the sides of large highways are breeding grounds for small animals. Hawks take advantage of this and perch on trees, highway fencing, or road signs, and watch the ground for mice, squirrels, snakes, frogs, and songbirds. The next time you are riding in a car on a long trip, see how many hawks you can spot. Where prey animals are abundant, you may see a hawk perched along the highway every few miles or so. Learn to identify the various hawks you see.

A hawk often shares its home range with an owl. The hawk hunts it during the day. The owl hunts at night. If you have a hawk living around you, you may also have a resident owl. One of the best ways to locate it in the daytime is to search the ground under evergreen trees for "owl pellets."

An owl often swallows its food whole. Undigestible bones and hair are eventually coughed up in the form of a pellet. This happens after the owl has roosted at the end of the night. When you find an owl's pellets, there is a good chance that the owl is sleeping in the tree above them. The size of a pellet is a clue to the size and type of owl you are looking for.

BARN OWL

SCREECH OWL

ALL PELLETS
ARE SHOWN
ACTUAL SIZE

SAW-WHET OWL

RED-TAILED HAWK

PERCHES HIGH ON TOP OF DEAD TREES, POWER LINE POLES, ETC.

RED~SHOULDERED HAWK

PREFERS TO PERCH ON THE LOWER BRANCHES OF TREES

SPARROW HAWK (KESTREL)

OFTEN PERCHES ON TELEPHONE WIRES AND ROAD SIGNS

MARSH HAWK

BOTH OF THESE HAWKS PERCH NEAR THE GROUND ON FENCE POSTS, TREE STUMPS, CLUMPS OF GRASS, ETC.

ROUGH-LEGGED HAWK

RACCOON USING A TRAIL

SQUIRRELS WILL GNAW AROUND THEIR HOLE TO KEEP IT FROM GROWING CLOSED

All wild animals leave telltale signs of their activities. Look for trails tramped along the ground. If you can bend over and walk along a trail without bumping into overhanging branches and twigs, you may be on a deer trail. If you must crawl to avoid being poked, the trail has been made by smaller animals, perhaps rabbits, foxes, raccoons, or skunks. Tiny inch-wide trails are pressed by the traveling feet of mice or voles.

Examine any digs, mounds, or scratches in the ground. A squirrel leaves a small dig where it has recovered a buried nut or seed. A skunk makes numerous little holes as it digs for grubs. A mole, tunneling close to the surface, creates a line of loosened earth and a small mound wherever it surfaces. Birds scratch ground debris away while searching for insects.

Little piles of emptied nut shells or stripped pinecones are more squirrel signs. A scattering of disheveled feathers means a bird has been eaten there by a predator.

Slender branch tips and winter buds bitten off cleanly are the work of browsing deer or rabbits. Buds that have been eaten into but not bitten off the branch are chickadee peckings or the nibblings of climbing deer mice. Saplings whose bark has been gnawed are evidence of rabbits, mice, or porcupines.

SQUIRREL DIG

MOLE MOUND

AN OPOSSUM
LIVING IN A
HOLLOW LOG
(LOOK FOR WHITE
OR SILVER HAIRS
ON LOG)

EVERGREEN
BUDS NIBBLED
INTO

A "girdle" of bare wood around the trunk of a large tree is a porcupine's doing. It has eaten all the bark from that spot. If a tree is chewed through and has fallen, you can be sure that you are in beaver territory. Beavers are the only wild animals that can fell trees.

If tree bark has been stripped or rubbed off, you will find no chew marks in the smooth, bared wood. Smooth bare spots on trees may have been made by a deer peeling the bark to eat it or, during the autumn mating season, by a feisty buck's rubbing its antlers on the tree.

Woodpeckers peck into trees to find and eat wood-boring insects. As the birds hammer, they knock away chips of wood. Look for little pieces of wood scattered on the ground around a tree. Then look up for the holes the chips came from.

When you find a hole in a tree, never reach inside. It could be a den tree, and you may get bitten by an animal who lives there. Do, however, look closely around the hole entrance to see if any hairs are caught on the bark. They are proof that the hole is occupied.

The surest identifying signs that animals leave are their footprints. In winter I follow the activities of the birds, mice, rabbits, foxes, coyotes, dogs, and cats around our farm. Day after day they scribble their stories in the snow. Each new snowfall hides a chapter of their lives.

A DOWNY
WOODPECKER
FEEDING ON
ANTS UNDER
LOOSE BARK

A YELLOW BIRCH
GIRDLED BY
A PORCUPINE

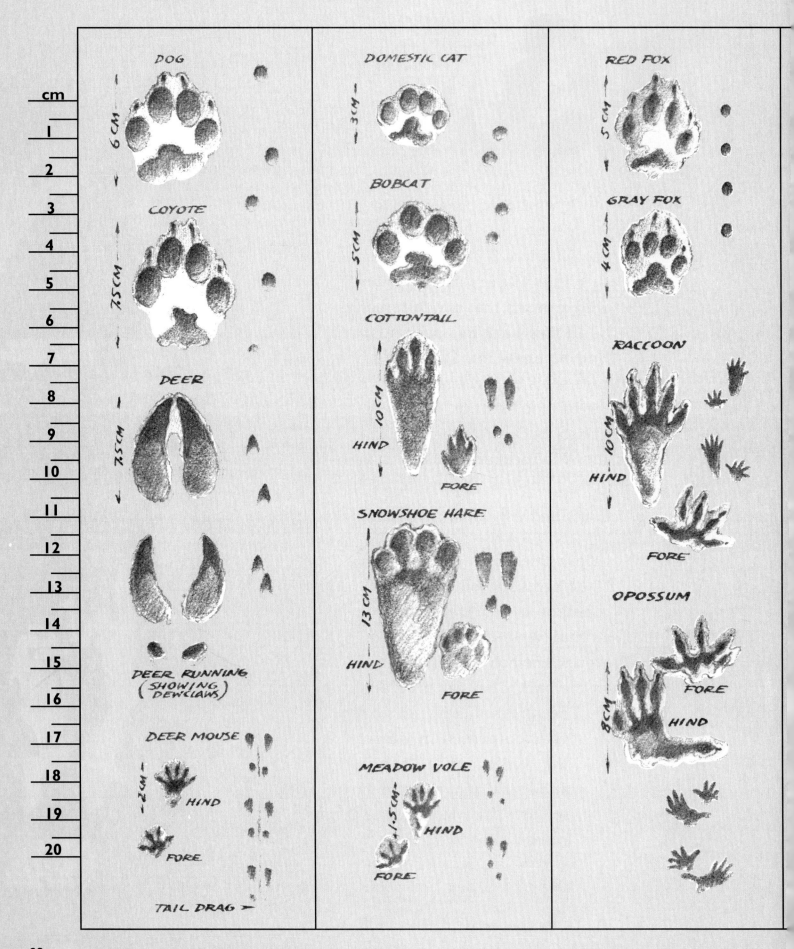

cm
1
2
3
4
5
6
7
8
9
10
11
12
13
14
15
16
17
18
19
20

DOG
6 CM

COYOTE
7.5 CM

DEER
7.5 CM

DEER RUNNING
(SHOWING
DEWCLAWS)

DEER MOUSE
2 CM
HIND
FORE

TAIL DRAG ➤

DOMESTIC CAT
3 CM

BOBCAT
5 CM

COTTONTAIL
10 CM
HIND
FORE

SNOWSHOE HARE
13 CM
HIND
FORE

MEADOW VOLE
1.5 CM
HIND
FORE

RED FOX
5 CM

GRAY FOX
4 CM

RACCOON
10 CM
HIND
FORE

OPOSSUM
8 CM
FORE
HIND

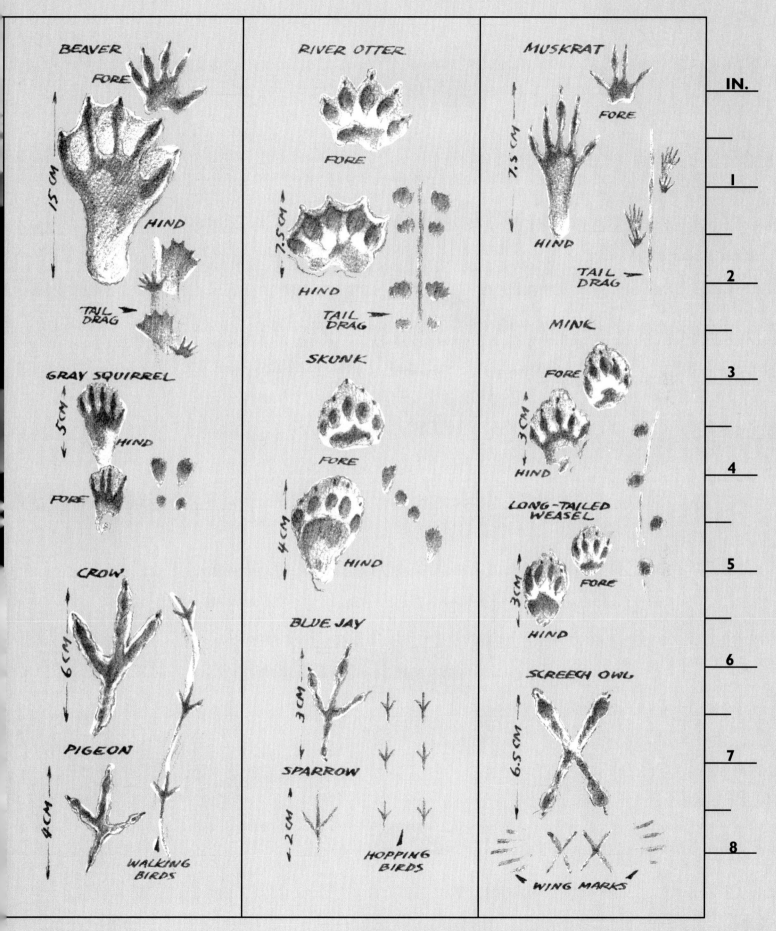

BEAVER
FORE
HIND
15 CM
TAIL DRAG

GRAY SQUIRREL
HIND
5 CM
FORE

CROW
6 CM

PIGEON
4 CM
WALKING BIRDS

RIVER OTTER
FORE
HIND
7.5 CM
TAIL DRAG

SKUNK
FORE
HIND
4 CM

BLUE JAY
3 CM

SPARROW
2 CM
HOPPING BIRDS

MUSKRAT
FORE
HIND
7.5 CM
TAIL DRAG

MINK
FORE
HIND
3 CM

LONG-TAILED WEASEL
FORE
HIND
3 CM

SCREECH OWL
6.5 CM
WING MARKS

IN.
1
2
3
4
5
6
7
8

NOTE: ALL TRACKS ARE SHOWN IN SNOW

99

SOURCE

Novel

AWARD WINNING

Book

from

THE MIDNIGHT FOX

By Betsy Byars
Illustrated by Peter Siu

It's summer and Tom is visiting his aunt, uncle, and cousin Hazeline on their farm. Tom thinks he will be bored—until he sees the black fox. The next few weeks, he spends his days in the woods watching the beautiful animal.

THE SEARCH

The days and weeks passed quickly, long warm days in which I walked through the woods looking for the black fox.

The next time I saw her was in the late afternoon at the ravine.

This was my favorite place in the forest. The sides of the ravine were heavy dark boulders with mosses and ferns growing between the rocks, and at the bottom were trunks of old dead trees. The tree trunks were like statues in some old jungle temple, idols that had fallen and broken and would soon be lost in the creeping foliage. There was only an occasional patch of sunlight.

At the top of the ravine was a flat ledge that stuck out over the rocks, and I was lying there on my stomach this particular afternoon. The rock was warm because the sun had been on it since noon, and I was half asleep when suddenly I saw something move below me. It was the black fox. There was a certain lightness, a quickness that I could not miss.

She came over the rocks as easily as a cat. Her tail was very high and full, like a sail that was bearing her forward. Her fur was black as coal, and when she was in the shadows all I could see was the white tip of her tail.

As I watched, she moved with great ease over one of the fallen trees, ran up the other side of the ravine, and disappeared into the underbrush.

I stayed exactly where I was. My head was resting on my arms, and everything was so still I could hear the ticking of my watch. I wanted to sit up. I am sort of a bony person and after I have been lying on something hard for a long time, I get very uncomfortable. This afternoon, however, I did not move; I had the feeling that the fox was going to come back through the ravine and I did not want to miss seeing her.

While I was waiting I watched an ant run across the ledge with an insect wing. He was running so fast with this wing that he would make a little breeze and the wing would fly out of his grasp. Then he would go back and get the wing and start running again.

Then I watched some birds on the other side of the ravine circling over the rocks, catching insects as they skimmed the air. It was a beautiful sight, and I thought as I watched them, *That* is what man had in mind when he first said, "I want to fly." And I thought about some old genius working up in a remote mountain valley actually making a little flying machine that he could strap on his back like a knapsack, and this old man would come down to a big air base and he would go out on the flight line and announce to everyone, "Folks, I have invented a flying machine." There would be a silence and then everyone would start laughing as if they would never stop, and finally the Captain would pause long enough to explain to the old man that flying machines had *already* been invented, that right over there—that big silver thing with the huge wings, *that* was a flying machine, and over there, those enormous bullet-shaped things, *those* were flying machines. "Well," the old man would say, shaking his head sadly, "I won't waste no more of your time. I'll just head on home," and he would press a button on his knapsack, and silently, easy as a bird, he would lift off the ground, and skimming the air, fly toward the hills. For a moment everyone would be too stunned to move, and then the General would cry, "Come back, come back," and everyone at the air base would run beneath the flying old man crying, "Wait, wait, come back, come back!" because that was the way every one of those men really wanted to fly, free and easy and silent as a bird. But the old man, who was a little hard of hearing, would not hear their cries and would fly off into the distance and never be seen again.

Right after I stopped thinking about this, the black fox came back. She came down the rocks the same way she had gone up, her white-tipped tail as light as a plume, and I remembered a black knight I saw once in the movies who was so tall and fine and brave you could see his black plume racing ahead of all the other knights when there was a battle.

She had something in her mouth that looked like a frog—it probably was, for the creek was low now and you could always find a frog if you wanted one. She trotted on, apparently concerned only with getting the frog home, and yet I had the feeling that she was missing nothing. She passed across the ravine in a zigzag line and then started up the other side.

I did not move, and yet all at once she looked up at me. She froze for a moment, her bright eyes looking at me with curiosity rather than fear, and she cocked her head to one side, listening.

I stayed perfectly still—I was getting good at this—and we looked at each other. Then she turned away and bounded up the side of the ravine, turning at the top and disappearing into the underbrush. I felt that somewhere in

the shelter of the trees she had paused to see if I was going to follow. Perhaps she wanted me to follow so she could lead me back into the forest, but I stayed where I was. After a while, I got up and went back to the farm.

The next time I saw the fox, it was a marvelous accident. These don't happen very often in real life, but they do happen, and that's what this was. Like the time Petie and I were walking down the alley behind his house and there, on top of this lady's garbage, we saw a mayonnaise jar full of marbles—not just cat's-eye marbles but all different kinds, kinds I had never seen before. Petie and I turned them all out on the grass and first Petie chose one and then I chose one until they were all gone. And both of us right now, today, have every single one of those marbles.

This was an even better accident. For the past two weeks I had been practically tearing the woods apart looking for the den of the black fox. I had poked under rocks and logs and stuck sticks in rotted trees, and it was a wonder that some animal had not come storming out and just bitten my hand off.

I had found a hornet's nest like a huge gray shield in a tree. I had found a bird's nest, low in a bush, with five pale-blue eggs and no mother to hatch them. I had found seven places where chipmunks lived. I had found a brown owl who never moved from one certain limb of one certain tree. I had heard a tree, split by lightning years ago, suddenly topple and crash to the ground, and I ran and got there in time to see a disgruntled possum run down the broken tree and into the woods. But I did not find the place where the black fox lived.

Now, on this day, I did not go into the woods at all. I had gone up the creek where there was an old chimney, all that was left of somebody's cabin. I had asked Aunt Millie about it, but all she could remember was that some people named Bowden had worked on the farm a long time ago and had lived here. I poked around the old chimney for a while because I was hoping I would find something that had belonged to the Bowdens, and then I gave that up and walked around the bend.

I sat on a rock, perfectly still, for a long time and looked down into the creek. There were crayfish in the water—I could see them, sometimes partly hidden beneath a covering of sand, or I could see the tips of their claws at the edge of a rock. There were fish in the water so small I could almost see through them. They stayed right together, these fish, and they moved together too.

After a while I looked across the creek and I saw a hollow where there was a small clearing. There was an outcropping of rocks behind the clearing and an old log slanted against the rocks. Soft grass sloped down to the creek bank.

I don't know how long I sat there—I usually forgot about my watch when I was in the woods—but it was a long time. I was just sitting, not expecting anything or waiting for anything. And the black fox came through the bushes.

She set a bird she was carrying on the ground and gave a small yapping bark, and at once, out of a hole beneath the rocks came a baby fox.

He did not look like his mother at all. He was tiny and woolly and he had a stubby nose. He tumbled out of the hole and fell on the bird as if he had not eaten in a month. I have never seen a fiercer fight in my life than the one that baby fox gave that dead bird. He shook it, pulled it, dragged it this way and that, all the while growling and looking about to see if anyone or anything was after his prize.

The black fox sat watching with an expression of great satisfaction. Mothers in a park sometimes watch their young children with this same fond, pleased expression. Her eyes were golden and very bright as she watched the tiny fox fall over the bird, rise, and shake it.

In his frenzy he dropped the bird, picked up an older dried bird wing in its place, and ran around the clearing. Then, realizing his mistake, he returned and began to shake the bird with even greater fierceness. After a bit he made another mistake, dropping the bird by his mother's tail, and then trying to run off with that.

In the midst of all this, there was a noise. It was on the other side of the clearing, but the black fox froze. She made a faint sound, and at once the baby fox, still carrying his bird, disappeared into the den.

The black fox moved back into the underbrush and waited. I could not see her but I knew she was waiting to lead the danger, if there was any, away from her baby. After a while I heard her bark from the woods, and I got up quietly and moved back down the creek. I did not want the black fox to see me and know that I had discovered her den.

Hazeline had told me that foxes will pick up their young like cats and take them away if they think someone has discovered their den.

I wondered if this was how the black fox had come to have only one baby. Perhaps her den had been the one discovered by Mr. Hunter. Perhaps she had started to move her cubs and had got only one to safety before Mr. Hunter had arrived with his dynamite.

I decided I would never come back here to bother her. I knew I would be tempted, because already I wanted to see that baby fox play with his bird some more, but I would not do it. If I was to see the black fox again, it would be in the woods, or in the pasture, or in the ravine, but I was not going to come to the den ever again. I did not know that an awful thing was going to happen which would cause me to break this resolution.

I went home and I put a tiny little mark on the edge of my suitcase with my penknife. I did this every time I saw the black fox. There were four marks on my suitcase

now, and in the weeks to come, there were to be ten more. Fourteen times I saw the black fox and most of those fourteen she saw me too. I think she knew that I wasn't anything to be afraid of. She didn't exactly jump with joy when she saw me and she didn't trust me, but I know she was not afraid.

After I got home, my mom said, "What on earth happened to your brand-new suitcase? There are notches all over it."

And I said, "Let me see," as if I was surprised too, but if I had wanted to, I could have sat right down then and told her about every one of those notches, that this one was for when I saw the black fox carrying home a live mouse so her baby could start learning to hunt for himself, and that this one was for when I saw the fox walking down the stream, her black legs shining like silk, and this one was for when the fox passed me so closely that I could have put out my hand and touched her thick soft fur.

How to

Make a Field Guide

Create a field guide for
a *close-up* look at **nature.**

A field guide is a great way to manage different kinds of information. It can be a book or a pamphlet that tells about the plant and animal life in an environment. Most guides contain a collection of facts, diagrams, and pictures. They put lots of information right at your fingertips. Create your own field guide for an outdoor place.

Terns on the beach.

sea lions
getting a
suntan

The
Pacific
Ocean

...e design
...oks like a
...tarfish.

dried
seaweed

Scallop
Shell

The sand
dollar's mouth

Sand from
Seal Beach

The sand dollar is a kind of sea urchin. When it's alive
it has lots of short spines all over its body. These
spines help it to burrow into the sand.

Go Exploring

Poison oak

Decide on the place you want to describe in your field guide. Before you go there, put on long pants and thick socks to protect your legs and feet from insects and poison ivy. When you get to your place, spend a few minutes just looking around. Soon you'll start to notice different plants and animals. Walk around and decide what specific area you want to describe in your guide.

Poison ivy

TOOLS

- notebook and pencil

- field guides, reference books, nature magazines

- paper, colored pencils, and markers

- magnifying glass

- protective clothing

- camera (optional)

Tips
- Be still so you don't scare the animals.
- Concentrate on one small area at a time.
- Use encyclopedias and field guides to identify plants and animals in your environment.
- If you have a camera, take some photos of the things you are observing.

2 Record What You Found

Get out your notebook and list the interesting things that you see. When you're done with your list, check off at least eight items that you want to include in your field guide. Write descriptions of each item, using lots of details. Make sketches and diagrams to help you remember what things look like.

How Am I Doing?

Before you put your field guide together, take a minute to ask yourself these questions:

● Did I write clear notes that will help me remember everything in my environment?

● Did I label my sketches?

● Have I identified the plants and animals I selected?

3 Make Your Guide

Now it's time to put your field guide together. Here are some ideas.

- Assembling the Pages: Attach several sheets of paper together to make a book, or fold one large sheet into thirds to create a brochure.

- The Cover: Create a title for your guide and add some art to make it come alive. Be sure to include your name.

- Pictures: Paste your sketches and diagrams onto the pages of your field guide. Having trouble drawing? Use reference books to identify the plants and animals you observed, and then trace the pictures from the books. You can also use pictures from magazines.

- Nature Facts: Write facts about each item on the pages of your book or brochure.

4 Present Your Guide

- Share your field guides with another class.

- Trade field guides with a friend. Visit the place someone else explored in his or her guide and see what you can learn!

If You Are Using a Computer ...

- Print out fun captions to add to your guide.
- Make a cover with the title page maker.

CONGRATULATIONS

You've learned several ways to record and organize information about nature. Now you'll be an informed nature watcher!

Veronica Gonzales-Vest
Park Ranger ▶

Glossary

al•gae (al′jē) *noun*
Simple plant life that lives in water. He saw green *algae* on the surface of the pond. ▲ **alga**

al•li•ga•tor (al′ i gā tər) *noun*
A large reptile with a long tail and a thick skin.

boul•ders (bōl′ dərz) *noun*
Huge rocks that are usually round and worn smooth by the wind and rain. ▲ **boulder**

bur•row (bur′ ō) *noun*
A hole or tunnel dug in the ground by an animal and used as shelter. The woodchuck ran into his *burrow*.

cy•press (sī′ prəs) *noun*
A kind of evergreen tree with small needles and woody cones.

cypress

e•gret (ē′ grit) *noun*
A kind of heron with white feathers.

eld•er (el′ dər) *noun*
Someone who is older and respected by the community. The mayor asked an *elder* for advice.

en•dan•gered (en dān′ jard) *adjective*
Threatened with extinction. Panthers are *endangered* animals.

ex•pe•di•tion (ek spi dish′ ən) *noun*
A long trip made for a specific purpose, such as exploration or research. They went on an *expedition* to the Antarctic.

Thesaurus

expedition
journey
tour
trip

fo•li•age (fō′ lē ij) *noun*
The leaves on plants or trees.

ham•mer•head (ham′ ər hed) *noun*
A kind of shark that has a hammer-shaped head.

hammerhead

egret

hol·low (hol′ ō) *noun*
An area of land that is lower than the land that surrounds it. The house was built in a *hollow*.

learned (lurnd) *verb*
Gained knowledge through study, practice, or experience. ▲ **learn**

ledge (lej) *noun*
A narrow surface that sticks out from a cliff like a shelf. The bird perched on the *ledge*.

leg·end (lej′ ənd)
noun
An inspiring story handed down from long ago.

Word History

Legend dates back to the 1300s, when it was used to mean "an inspiring story about the life of a great person." Later, it came to mean "any inspiring story from long ago." Today we use both meanings of the word.

lodge (loj) *noun*
A type of Native American dwelling.

Word Study

Memory comes from the Latin word *memoria*, which means "memory." Several other words use the Latin root *memo*. A *memoir* is a kind of autobiography; a *memento* is a souvenir of a place or a person; and a *memorial* is something that helps people remember an important event or person.

---

mem·o·ry
(mem′ ə rē) *noun*
The ability to remember things.

moss·es
(môs′ iz) *noun*
Tiny green plants that form a covering like a mat on damp ground and rocks. ▲ **moss**

na·tion·al park
(nash′ə nl park) *noun*
An area of land set aside and preserved by the federal government for the public to visit.

nat·u·ral·ist
(nach′ər ə list) *noun*
A person who studies plants and animals.

a	add	o͞o	took	ə =
ā	ace	o͞o	pool	a in *above*
â	care	u	up	e in *sicken*
ä	palm	û	burn	i in *possible*
e	end	yo͞o	fuse	o in *melon*
ē	equal	oi	oil	u in *circus*
i	it	ou	pout	
ī	ice	ng	ring	
o	odd	th	thin	
ō	open	th	this	
ô	order	zh	vision	

Glossary

out·crop·ping
(out´ krop ing) *noun*
The part of a rock that is
above the surface of the
ground. There was an
outcropping of rocks near
the lake.

park rang·er
(park rān´ jər) *noun*
A person whose job it is
to take care of a park.

pred·a·tor
(pred´ ə tər) *noun*
An animal that hunts
other animals for food.

prey (prā) *noun*
An animal that is hunted
by other animals as food.

rac·coon
(ra kōōn´) *noun*
A small, tree-climbing
animal with black mask-
like markings on its face
and a bushy, ringed tail.

range (rānj) *noun*
An area of land on
which an animal lives.
The rabbit's *range* was
a couple of acres.

ra·vine (rə vēn´) *noun*
A deep, narrow valley.

re·search
(ri sûrch´) *noun*
Close and careful study
of a subject.

rook·er·y
(rōōk´ ə rē) *noun*
A breeding place or
colony of birds.

sanc·tu·ar·ies
(sangk´ chōō er ēz)
noun
Places where wildlife is
protected and hunting is
illegal. ▲ **sanctuary**

saw grass (sô gras)
noun
A kind of plant with
grasslike leaves that are
edged with sharp spines.

scu·ba dive
(skōō´ bə dīv) *verb*
To swim underwater
wearing scuba gear.

raccoon

se·quoi·a
(si kwoi′ə) *noun*
A very tall kind of ever-green tree that grows in California and has large cones.

site (sīt) *noun*
The place where something is located. The Liberty Bell is a famous *site*.

snor·kel
(snôr′ kəl) *verb*
To swim underwater with a mask and a tube that allows breathing. The kids *snorkel* along the reef in the bay.

ter·ri·to·ry
(ter′ i tôr ē) *noun*
An area of land that belongs to a particular animal that defends it against other animals.

tracks (trakz) *noun*
Marks left by animals. The naturalist followed the rabbit's *tracks* to its burrow. ▲ **track**

trail (trāl) *noun*
A path.

tracks

un·der·brush
(un′dər brush) *noun*
Shrubs or bushes that grow under tall trees in a forest area.

Thesaurus
underbrush
bush
shrubbery
thicket

voy·age
(voi′ ij) *noun*
A long journey, such as one made on a ship.

wild·life
(wīld′ līf′) *noun*
Wild plants and animals that live in their natural surroundings.

a	add	o͝o	took	ə =
ā	ace	o͞o	pool	a in *above*
â	care	u	up	e in *sicken*
ä	palm	û	burn	i in *possible*
e	end	yo͞o	fuse	o in *melon*
ē	equal	oi	oil	u in *circus*
i	it	ou	pout	
ī	ice	ng	ring	
o	odd	th	thin	
ō	open	ŧh	this	
ô	order	zh	vision	

Authors & Illustrators

Jim Arnosky *pages 90–99*

When not outside fishing or hiking, this author-illustrator can usually be found at his drawing table or at work on his journals, recording wildlife discoveries.

When he talks about his book, *Secrets of a Wildlife Watcher,* he compares it to a conch shell. "The sea isn't inside the conch," he explains, "but the conch brings it to you." In the same way, he says, his book isn't filled with real trees or birds. But it still brings nature to its readers.

Joseph Bruchac *pages 60–71*

When Joseph Bruchac was a small boy, his *Abenaki* grandfather taught him how to walk quietly in the woods and how to fish. His grandmother encouraged his love of reading. Bruchac says, "It wasn't until I was grown, and had children of my own, that I turned to telling traditional Native American stories. I wanted to share those stories with my sons, so I started to write them down."

Bruchac's advice to beginning writers is, "Do it a page at a time, and keep doing it. You take one step to climb a mountain."

Betsy Byars *pages 100–113*

Newbery-medalist Betsy Byars has written over 25 books but her favorite is still *The Midnight Fox.* "I was walking in the woods near our cabin," she recalls, "and I came upon a fox. It wasn't a black fox, but it was a stunning moment for me. I looked at that fox, and the fox looked at me, for what seemed like an eternity—though it couldn't have been because I held my breath the whole time."

Jean Craighead George *pages 10–21*

This author has studied nature her entire life. As a hobby, she cares for wild animals around her home. "These wild animals depart in autumn when they feel the urge to migrate," Jean George explains. "While they are here, however, they become characters in my stories."

Johanna Hurwitz *pages 28–41*

Like Ali Baba, Johanna Hurwitz not only grew up in New York City, she's also visited national parks hoping to spot a bear. Though she never did see a bear on any of these trips, she has had better luck in her own backyard. Once she spotted a bear right outside her home in Vermont!

Ann McGovern *pages 48–59*

As a child, this nature lover never imagined she would go hot-air ballooning over France.

"Because I was shy, I didn't like to speak. So, I began writing," she admits. But not anymore! Today Ann McGovern frequently gives speeches at schools and national conferences.

Books &

Author Study

More by
Jean Craighead George

The Fire Bug Connection: An Ecological Mystery
Maggie and Mitch don't know why the fire bugs are dying out. But they are determined to find out, and save these rare insects from extinction.

One Day in the Desert
Bird Wing, a Papago girl, and her mother live in the Sonoran Desert. What will they do when a mountain lion takes shelter in their home?

Moon of the Deer
What does it take for a deer to survive in the wild? This book explores the relationship between the deer and the other animals that share its habitat.

Fiction

The Adventures of Spider
by Joyce Arkhurst
illustrated by Jerry Pinkney
Spider is always getting himself into and out of trouble! Here are six funny stories about this West African trickster.

The Cricket in Times Square
by George Selden
illustrated by Garth Williams
This classic novel uses humor and animal characters to tell a story about true friendship.

A Llama in the Family
by Johanna Hurwitz
Llamas are usually found in Peru. What will happen when a llama comes to live with a Vermont family?

Nonfiction

The Animal Atlas
by Barbara Taylor
illustrated by Kenneth Lilly
This guide to the world's wildlife is packed with lifelike illustrations, helpful maps, and amazing facts.

Crinkleroot's Guide to Knowing the Birds
by Jim Arnosky
No one knows nature like Crinkleroot. In this book, he shares his secrets for identifying all kinds of birds.

Storms
by Seymour Simon
This book uses dramatic photos as well as scientific information to make it easy to understand how storms occur.

&Media

Videos

The Bear
Columbia Pictures
The stars of this film are an orphaned bear cub and the huge grizzly who befriends him. Together they face many challenges, including a meeting with their most dangerous enemy: humans. (93 minutes)

How the Leopard Got His Spots
Rabbit Ears
Here's a new way of looking at an old story. This animated version of Rudyard Kipling's classic features the voice of actor Danny Glover. (30 minutes)

Search for the Great Apes
National Geographic Videos
Watch as scientist Birute Galdikas-Brindamour tries to help a baby orangutan born in captivity adjust to life in the wild. (60 minutes)

Software

Earthquest: Explore Ecology
Davidson
Travel to a Brazilian rain forest, build food webs, solve puzzles, and more, as you learn how plants and animals live within an ecosystem.

Mammals: A Multimedia Encyclopedia
National Geographic
Use articles, sound clips, video footage, and color graphics to find information on more than 200 mammals in this unique reference source.

Whales: Audubon Wildlife Adventures
Softkat
How do whales communicate with each other? How do they find their way across the sea? Find out when you participate in four whale adventures.

Magazines

Ranger Rick
National Wildlife Federation
Every issue of this award-winning magazine is packed with photos and articles about animals and their habitats.

Zoobooks
Wildlife Education, Ltd.
Each zoobook offers an in-depth look at one particular animal.

A Place to Write

When's the best time to see geysers spout at Yellowstone? Where are the best places to hike? Find out more by requesting brochures and maps from:
National Park Service
P.O. Box 37127
Washington, D.C.
20013-7127

IT TAKES A LEADER

Over 1,200 new words!

Weber's Dictionary

3rd Edition

COMPACT CASSETTE TAPE
RECORDER

CHILDREN'S EXPRESS

SUKI CHEONG
EDITOR

30 Cooper Square, 4th Floor
New York, New York 10003
Tel: (212) 505-7777

IS AN AUTHORIZED REPRESENTATIVE
FOR THE CHILDREN'S EXPRESS NEWS
SERVICE. WE WILL GREATLY
APPRECIATE ANY AND ALL
COURTESIES, PASSES, AND AID THAT
YOU CAN PROVIDE.

AUTHORIZATION

Explore
a Newspaper Office

In every community there are people who inspire others to take action.

Taking Charge

People take action on issues that matter to them.

Spread the Word

People communicate on the important issues of the day.

AMERICAN RED CROSS
Radio: 30
Live Announcer Script

V.O.: Somewhere in the country...this very
day...disaster struck. In fact, disaster strikes
every single day. Which means every single
night someone needs food, shelter, and a
place to rest. You can make a difference.
Please support the American Red Cross.

Ideas in Action

It takes leadership and an organized effort to reach our goals.

Trade Books

The following books accompany this *It Takes a Leader* SourceBook.

Realistic Fiction

Class President

by Johanna
Hurwitz
illustrated by
Sheila Hamanaka

Environmental Fantasy

**The Great
Squirrel
Uprising**

by Dan Elish
illustrated by
Denys Cazet

Historical Fiction

**Sweet Clara and the
Freedom Quilt**

by Deborah
Hopkinson
illustrated by
James Ransome

Biography

**Where Was
Patrick
Henry on
the 29th
of May?**

by Jean Fritz
illustrated by
Margot Tomes

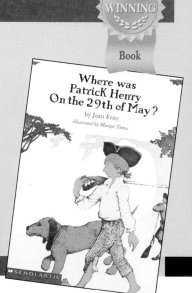

Taking Charge

Celebrate the lives of twelve African-American women as their portraits come to life.

Travel back to prehistoric times and meet Oog, a man ahead of his time. Then read about a young Native American who works for her community.

WORKSHOP 1

Take a poll and find out what people think about important issues.

School
Litter
POLL

9

Dinner at Aunt

by Faith Ringgold

AWARD WINNING

Book

My aunt Connie is a great artist. She and Uncle Bates live in a big beautiful house on the beach in Sag Harbor, Long Island. Every summer they invite our whole family to come for a delicious dinner and a special showing of Aunt Connie's artwork. I could hardly wait for this year's dinner—not only for the food but also for the art, which was to be a big surprise.

Connie's House

Another surprise was Lonnie, my aunt and uncle's adopted son. I fell in love with him the first time I saw him. Have you ever seen a little black boy with red hair and green eyes? Neither had I before Lonnie. While the rest of the family relaxed on the beach before dinner, Lonnie and I went in the house and played hide-and-seek.

I heard some noises up in the attic and climbed the stairs to
see if Lonnie was up there.

"Come out, come out, wherever you are," I sang out.

"Come in, Melody," a strange voice answered. "We would like
to talk to you."

"Lonnie, stop trying to scare me with that strange voice,"
I said.

I peeked into the attic and saw twelve beautiful paintings. I knew I had found Aunt Connie's surprise.

"Lonnie," I yelled, "please come out of your hiding place."

"Melody," Lonnie answered, "I am right beside you, and I heard that strange voice, too."

"Aunt Connie's paintings can talk, Lonnie."

"Paintings don't talk, Melody. Only the artist can speak."

"Yes, we can speak, Lonnie," the voice said.

"Who are you?" we chimed in chorus as we held hands and entered the strange room.

"I will be the first to speak. I am Rosa Parks. I was born in 1913 in Alabama. I am called the mother of the civil rights movement. In 1955, I was arrested for refusing to sit in the back of the bus. That incident started the Montgomery bus boycott and inspired Martin Luther King, Jr., to devote his life to the civil rights movement."

"But how can you speak? Paintings don't talk like people," Lonnie said.

"Your aunt Connie created us to tell you the history of our struggle. Would you like to hear more?"

We nodded, and the next painting spoke.

"I am Fannie Lou Hamer, born in 1917 in Mississippi. I was a civil rights activist and public speaker. I worked with Martin Luther King for voters' rights in the South. I helped thousands of people register to vote."

"My dream was education. I am Mary McLeod Bethune, born in 1875 in South Carolina. I founded Bethune-Cookman College. I was a special adviser to Presidents Franklin D. Roosevelt and Harry S. Truman and founded the National Council of Negro Women, an organization that has more than one million members."

"I was a sculptor. My name is Augusta Savage, and I was born in 1892 in Florida. I founded The Savage Studio of Arts and Crafts in Harlem. I taught many artists to paint, draw, and sculpt. Maybe you've heard of one of my students, the famous painter Jacob Lawrence?"

"My name is Dorothy Dandridge. Born in 1922 in Ohio, I was the first African-American actress to become a Hollywood star. I was nominated for an Academy Award in 1954 for Best Actress for the film *Carmen Jones*. I starred in other films with famous actors such as James Mason and Joan Fontaine."

"I am Zora Neale Hurston, born in 1901 in Florida."

"I know who you are," I said. "You're a famous writer."

"Yes, Melody. In the 1930s I was the most prolific African-American writer. My books—*Their Eyes Were Watching God*, *Moses, Man of the Mountain*, and *Mules and Men*—are considered among the best examples of American writing."

"I was born way back in 1803 in Connecticut. My name is Maria W. Stewart. Back then, women could not be public speakers, yet I spoke out for the human rights of oppressed blacks. I was also the first African American to lecture in defense of women's rights."

"I am Bessie Smith, empress of blues. I was born in 1894 in Tennessee. I was once the highest paid African-American artist in the world. The great jazz trumpeter Louis Armstrong was one of my accompanists. I inspired many singers with my soul and spirit."

"People called me Moses. I am Harriet Tubman, born in 1820 in Maryland. I brought more than three hundred slaves to freedom in the North in nineteen trips on the Underground Railroad— and never lost a passenger. Among them were my aged mother and father and my ten brothers and sisters."

"I am Sojourner Truth, born in 1797 in New York State. I was an itinerant preacher and an abolitionist with Frederick Douglass and William Lloyd Garrison. I spoke out for women's rights during slavery, when no American woman had the right to vote. I met and spoke with President Abraham Lincoln."

"I am Marian Anderson, born in 1902 in Pennsylvania. Arturo Toscanini, the great conductor, said a voice such as mine is heard only once in a hundred years. I was denied the right to sing at Constitution Hall by the Daughters of the American Revolution in Washington, D.C. In protest, I sang on the steps of the Lincoln Memorial to a crowd of 75,000. I was known as the world's greatest living contralto and was the first African American to perform with the Metropolitan Opera Company."

"Someday I want to be an opera singer, too," Lonnie said.

"My name is Madame C.J. Walker. I was born in 1867 in Louisiana. I was the first self-made American woman millionaire. I employed more than three thousand people in my cosmetics company. My invention, the hair-straightening comb, changed the appearance of millions of people."

"What do you think of us, children?" the paintings asked.

"I am very proud to be an African-American woman," I said.

"You are only a nine year old, Melody, not a woman," Lonnie said.

"And who do you think you are, Lonnie, with your red hair and green eyes? Not many African Americans look like you!"

"My hair is red and my eyes are green, but I am black, ten years old, and just as proud as you to be African American!"

Just then Uncle Bates appeared at the attic door.

"Since you two have already discovered Aunt Connie's surprise, you can help me take the paintings down to hang in the dining room."

Lonnie and I helped Uncle Bates hang the paintings on the dining room walls, then Aunt Connie called the family to dinner to see the big surprise.

Grandpa Bates was our family's toastmaster. Last year he toasted my sister Dee Dee and her fiancé, Carl's, engagement. Today he toasted Lonnie, who was Aunt Connie and Uncle Bates's son from now on. Then Lonnie read an African proverb in Swahili: "*Mti mzuri huota kwenye miiba,*" "A good tree grows among thorns." Aunt Connie's smile told us she knew we had been talking to the paintings.

Lonnie and I winked back at her, keeping the secret.

Aunt Connie's dinners are the best. We had roast turkey, duck, cranberry sauce, corn bread, stuffing, macaroni and cheese, candied sweet potatoes, and fresh greens. Seated around the table were the usual people: Aunt Connie and Uncle Bates, my mother and father, Grandma and Grandpa Bates, my sister Dee Dee and her new husband, Carl, and Mr. and Mrs. Tucker. But only Lonnie and I knew that today's dinner was extra special. It was magical. As we ate, Aunt Connie spoke about each of the women in her portraits.

Aunt Connie's paintings were no longer hanging on the dining room walls but sitting in the chairs around the table as our dinner guests. Aunt Connie's voice faded into the background, and our

family disappeared as Sojourner Truth spoke in support of the women's vote:

"Look at me . . . . I have plowed and planted and gathered into barns and no man could head me . . . I have borne thirteen children and seen most all sold into slavery, and when I cried out a mother's grief, none but Jesus heard me. And ain't I a woman?"

Harriet Tubman spoke about slavery: "There was one of two things I had a right to, liberty or death; if I could not have one, I would have the other, for no man should take me alive."

Maria Stewart spoke next, about a woman's right to speak in public. "Men of eminence have mostly risen from obscurity; nor will I, although female of a darker hue and far more obscure than they, bend my head or hang my harp upon willows, for though poor I will virtuous prove."

"Connie, your art is a great inspiration to us all," said Uncle Bates.

"Their lives speak more powerfully than any paintings could," Aunt Connie said. "Don't you think so children?" She winked her eye at Lonnie and me.

"When I grow up, I want to sing in opera houses all over the world. I know it will be hard, but not as hard for me as it was for Marian Anderson," said Lonnie.

"I want to be the president of the United States when I grow up," I said, "so I can change some of the things that make people's lives so sad. I know I can do it because of these women."

"Amen! Amen!" everybody chimed.

"I never thought my wife and the mother of our children would be the president of the United States," Lonnie whispered in my ear.

"And I never thought I would marry an African-American opera singer with red hair and green eyes," I whispered back.

"But what will our children think of Aunt Connie's secret, Melody?"

"Our children will love the secret. We will have delicious family dinners, and they will be magical just like Aunt Connie's, and our children, Lonnie, will be just like us."

from
The Big Book for Our Planet

The Last Days of the Giddywit

by
Natalie Babbitt

illustrated by
Steven Kellogg

THE
PREHISTORIC
MUSEUM

A Giddywit battling a fly.

Years and years ago, in the time when houses were caves—this was after the dinosaurs but a while before shovels—there was a tribe of people called the Giddywit. They lived all together, and every day the men would go out and hunt supper while the women stayed home to pick nuts and berries and teach the babies how to swat flies. Then at night, when the men came back, everyone would feast on mammoth meat or reindeer, with a side of the nuts and berries, and they tossed the garbage in a corner.

After a few weeks, of course, the pile of garbage would get pretty big and smelly, and the flies were something fierce, so the Giddywit would pack up their furs and clubs, and the babies' bibs and swatters, and move to a new cave. This always caused great confusion, with snarling and arguments, and once in a while a baby would get left behind and have to be fetched. But soon the Giddywit would be settled again in a nice fresh place and could start over, tossing garbage and swatting flies.

Now, there was among the Giddywit a thin little man named Oog who wasn't allowed to hunt mammoths because he only got in the way. So his job was to look for eggs. He was good at climbing trees, way up where the nests were, and while he was up there, he would look out over the land where everything was wild and sweet and didn't ever seem to get smelly. "This is nice," he would say to himself. "I wish *we*

34

could live in trees." But they couldn't because of having to hang on, even while sound asleep, which would have been hard for everyone, especially the babies. Still, Oog thought a lot about how nice it was, far away from the garbage.

One night in the cave—it was summer, and the flies and the garbage were atrocious—Oog said to everyone, "Why don't we try putting the garbage outside?"

"Outside?" said everyone. "You're a dope, Oog. If you want to bring every bear and tiger in the neighborhood nosing around the door, that's the way to do it." And they snickered at Oog and poked each other with their elbows and winked.

"We could dig holes and bury the garbage, maybe," said Oog.

"Who's got time to dig holes?" they said, with more snickers and winks. "Sure, if we had a shovel. But it's still a while before shovels. And anyway, what's wrong with moving to a new cave?"

"We might run out of caves," said Oog.

"Run out of caves!" they cried. "You're a dope, Oog." And they winked and poked each other again and threw more garbage in a corner, and then they lay down on their furs and went to sleep.

But Oog sat up, swatting flies, and thought it over. And the next morning, instead of climbing trees to look for eggs, he took Mrs. Oog by the hand and went away, a long way off, miles and miles through the wild, sweet land, and came after many days to a little cave just right for two. "This is the ticket," he said to Mrs. Oog. "We'll live on nuts and berries and the very occasional rabbit, and of course we'll always have eggs. And we'll never throw garbage into corners."

"But, dear," said Mrs. Oog, "what will we *do* with the garbage? We'll have to put it *some*where."

"We'll bury it," said Oog.

"But, dear," said Mrs. Oog, "we can't do that without shovels to dig the holes."

"We won't need very big holes," said Oog. "Not with only two. So I shall invent the spoon and dig with that."

"Clever," said Mrs. Oog. "And I shall invent the fork. To keep our fingers clean at supper. It's time."

So Oog and Mrs. Oog invented the spoon and fork and buried their garbage outside the cave, and everything stayed nice and clean, and they were happy as clams even though they'd never seen a clam, until one day, a year or so later, here came the rest of the Giddywit, tramping along with their furs and babies, arguing and snarling.

"Well, well," said Oog. "What brings the lot of you to *these* far parts?"

"We ran out of caves," said everyone. "And now you're going to snicker, aren't you?"

"No," said Oog, "but maybe you've learned that you have to bury your garbage."

"Can't do it," said everyone. "It's still too long before shovels."

"Maybe so," said Oog, "but I've invented the spoon, which is pretty good for digging."

"Oog," they said, "you're still a dope. Digging with a—what did you call it? A spoon?—is too much work for the kind of hole *we'd* need. We'll just go on and look for another bunch of caves."

So they did, still snarling and arguing, and Oog never saw them again, except, as it happens, for the babies. For the Giddywit found a new cave farther on and settled down to tossing and swatting. And then one night, when the wind was in the right direction, some bears and tigers sniffed out the cave and finished off the Giddywit, except for the babies, and left no garbage at all. The babies found their way back to Oog and Mrs. Oog, who, having no babies of their own, were delighted. And Oog made a great big spoon to dig holes with, so that shovels were invented at last, because what is a shovel but a great big spoon?

So that was the end of the Giddywit and the start of the Oogites, a neat and tidy tribe from which we are all descended.

Maybe.

SOURCE
ZuZu
Newspaper

from
ZuZu
JOUR

Eye on the Prize

NAL

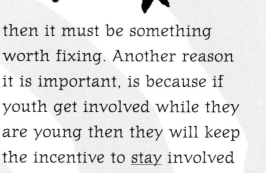

Hi, my name is Rhiannon Chavis-Legerton. I am from a small town in the south-eastern part of North Carolina called Pembroke. I am a 13-year-old Lumbee Indian who has lived here all of my life. My family works in the community for justice, equality, and for correct treatment of the environment. Our organization is called the Center for Community Action.

I have been taught that youth should be involved with community work. Over time, I have grown to understand why this is so. The reason I think so is because youth have a strong say in the community. Many government officials will sometimes listen to youth more than they would adults. They figure that if the youth are strong enough to speak out

then it must be something worth fixing. Another reason it is important, is because if youth get involved while they are young then they will keep the incentive to <u>stay</u> involved as adults.

Before you can become fully involved, there will be many obstacles to overcome in the process. One of these is to ignore all of the remarks thrown at you by other people such as, "You won't win, why not just give up trying?" Over time, you will find that the only reason people say things like this is because they are really scared that you will win. Another obstacle is that if you have one teeny tiny bit of concern that you will have to work with people of other races, then get rid of it right away.

Eye on the Prize

This is because when you are fighting for something right, then it is most likely that people from other races are too. But over time, you will see that they have the same thoughts and ideas as you do.

I have done much work for change. Right now I will tell you about some of it. When I was about 5 years old, threats were made that an incinerator would be put near my home. My family and many other families worked and planned together to think of a way to stop it.

There was something for everyone to do, young and old. I have also been to Alabama to help the Choctaw stop a waste dump. I gave a speech there that was quoted on TV and in the newspaper. I am now in a multi-cultural play about a time in Robeson County when there was a lot of hatred and prejudice against people of color.

If anyone reading would like to get involved, here are some starting tips. Keep an update on the problems going on in your community. Always keep a cool head and don't blow your top every time something doesn't go your way. Go in expecting to win, and if you do, praise yourself, but don't get a big head because it might affect your attitude on the next issue. And the last tip I have is give all you can to the work and cooperate with others.

Since I have been fighting for people's rights, I have found it easier to do if you live by certain sayings.

The first one is to never give up, your luck will turn around one day.

The next one is to always look ahead, never dwell in the past or you will accomplish nothing.

The last thing that I live by is to keep your eyes on the prize, the light is never too bright.

"...Get Everyone involved including children, because if they're not they might have bad dreams or thoughts because they hear you talking about it. They don't understand what is happening. So... just REMEMBER - if you have them, (KIDS) INVOLVE THEM!"
— excerpt from a speech by Rhiannon (when she was 11-yrs old!)

How to
Take a Public Opinion Poll

Choose a question that affects everyone.

When an organization or a town council wants to know how a community feels about an issue, it often takes a public opinion poll.

Give more than one answer.

What's a public opinion poll? A public opinion poll is the collection of answers to questions about important issues or events. To make the poll as accurate as possible, different kinds of people are asked the same question. A pollster questions both younger and older people. The results of a public opinion poll are often summarized in a bar graph.

Ask a follow-up question, if it is appropriate.

School Litter POLL

The poll should have a title.

Do you think litter is a problem at school?

If so, is it worse in the playground?

Classroom?

Are there enough trash cans provided?

Do you ever litter?

1 Decide on a Question

Choose a question on a topic that affects your classroom, school, or community. It should be a question with many possible answers; for example, how can your class work together to help your community? What charity should your school have a fundraiser for? What should your town build on the vacant lot on Main Street? After you pick your question, make up four to six possible answers.

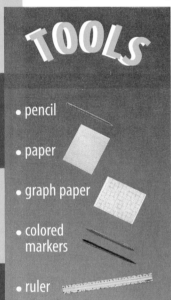

TOOLS

- pencil
- paper
- graph paper
- colored markers
- ruler

2 Create a Poll Sheet

Make a chart, and write your poll question at the top. Then put at least four possible answers to your question on the left-hand side of the page. Leave enough room between each answer so that you can fill in people's responses. Don't forget to leave a space labeled *other* to record answers you haven't thought of.

What should our town build on the vacant lot?

an in-line skating park ~~|||| |||| ||||~~ ||

tennis courts ~~||||~~ |

basketball courts ~~||||~~ ~~||||~~

3 Take a Poll

Ask at least ten people to answer your poll question. Try to ask a variety of people. For example, you can ask your classmates, teachers, neighbors, and family members. Record everyone's answers on your chart.

Tips
- Poll different types of people to get different opinions.
- Be polite when you ask people for their opinion.
- Mark down each answer right away so that you don't forget it.

4 Make a Bar Graph

Graph the results of your poll. Share the graph with your classmates.

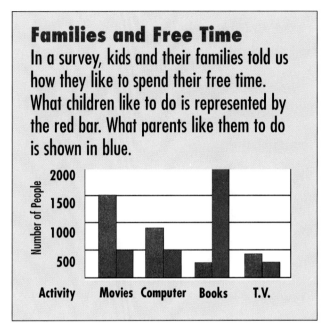

Families and Free Time
In a survey, kids and their families told us how they like to spend their free time. What children like to do is represented by the red bar. What parents like them to do is shown in blue.

If You Are Using a Computer ...

This is a good opportunity to create a poll to share on-line. You can print out the answers and then create your bar graph.

THINK

Why is it important to know how others in the community feel about a certain issue?

Suki Cheong
Editor ▶

People communicate on the important issues of the day.

Spread the Word

Meet Mother Jones as she helps miners and their families stand up for their rights.

Join nine-year-old James Ale as he lobbies the mayor to build a park.

Visit Suki Cheong, an editor at *Children's Express.*

WORKSHOP 2

Pick a cause you care about and write a public service announcement.

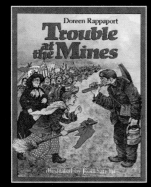
from

Trouble
at the
Mines

AWARD WINNING

Book

by Doreen Rappaport
illustrated by Dom Lee

In 1899 the coal miners in Arnot, Pennsylvania went on strike. They hadn't had a raise in seven years and could no longer support their families. Mother Jones, a famous union organizer, promised to lead the miners and their families to victory. Ten-year-old Rosie Wilson and her cousin Mary were determined to march with Mother Jones.

OCTOBER 15, 1899

Hundreds of people were sitting in the open field outside the town waiting for the union meeting to begin. Most of them were shouting at each other.

Uncle Jack was yelling at Rosie's father. "It's four months since this strike began. Over four hundred miners have left town, and every day more are leaving. Soon there won't be any union members left. We've got to go back to work, Bryan."

"We'll never get a raise if we go back."

"Brother, if this strike continues, there's not going to be anybody left in town to use the raise."

Rosie's father grabbed his brother's forearm. "Jack, we're close to winning. All the miners in towns around are out on strike. Production is crippled. If the mine owners don't give in soon, they won't be able to get the coal for winter. We just *have* to hold out a little longer."

"Lincoln told me they've got enough coal stocked from last spring to sell through this winter. They don't need us," shouted Uncle Jack. "He also told me that if this strike continues, the mine owners are going to close the mines permanently. Then we won't need a union."

"Lincoln tells you a story, and you believe him. You're a fool, Jack." Rosie's father raised his clenched fist so near Uncle Jack's face that Rosie and Mary were sure he was going to punch him.

"You're the fool, Bryan," said Uncle Jack. He turned and marched to the front of the gathering. "Friends, friends!" he shouted. "It's been four months since the strike began. Four months ago we had a little money, and there were plenty of vegetables in the garden. Now it's almost November and we have only cabbages and sprouts left. We have no money. We can't buy food for our families. We can't pay our rent. Winter's almost here. We can't get coal to heat our houses. We have no choice but to go back to work before our families starve and freeze to death!"

Uncle Jack held up a piece of paper. "See this paper? One hundred miners, two ministers, the town doctor, the druggist, the teacher . . . signed this petition asking the owners to open the mines so we can go back to work. They've agreed. Tomorrow morning the mines will be open and anyone who wants to go back to work can. I say it's time to go back to work, before we all starve."

Rosie's mother sprang to her feet. "Don't listen to Jack," she pleaded. "If you go back now, the mine owners will never give you a raise."

Aunt Sally stood up. "I think Jack is wrong. Things will only get better if we stick together. We can't buckle under to the mine owners."

Uncle Jack hollered. "Shut up, woman. If we don't go back tomorrow, the company will shut the mines down permanently, and we won't have any jobs to go back to."

"Mine owners always threaten to close the mines down when miners ask for what they deserve!" Aunt Sally yelled back.

"What do *you* know?" Uncle Jack shouted. "You're a woman, not a miner."

Rosie's mother pointed her finger at Uncle Jack. "Scab!"

"Fool!" Uncle Jack yelled.

"Scab!"

"Fool!"

Everyone began shouting at each other. The yelling accelerated to a roar. Only Rosie's father was quiet. He scanned the crowd frantically. "Who are you looking for, Pa?" asked Rosie, pulling on his arm.

"She's come," he whispered suddenly, pointing to an old woman walking slowly across the field toward Uncle Jack.

The woman was short, with thick round glasses, a round face and a round body. Her white hair was covered by a wide-brimmed hat. She wore a long-sleeved black dress with a frilly collar.

By the time she reached Uncle Jack, the shouting had stopped. "What do you think, Mother Jones?" Rosie's father called out to her. "What should we do?"

Mother Jones clasped her hands and looked up as if in prayer. Then she looked out at the crowd, and her face broke into a slow grin. "Well," she said, "the first thing I think we should do is straighten Jack out. He's forgotten how important women are. He wouldn't be here today if it hadn't been for his mother."

Rosie and Mary looked at each other and giggled.

Amens and shrieks of laughter sounded all around them.

Her smile disappeared. "Jack has also forgotten how a miner's wife bids good-bye to her husband and sons every morning, never knowing if they'll be carried home mangled or dead. How she has to live in an overcrowded shack that's always dirty from coal dust. How she has to juggle her husband's meager wages to feed and clothe her family. And if her husband is injured, how she has to go back to work fourteen hours a day in the mills, and still cook, clean and raise the family. How can anyone believe that this strike isn't as much a woman's business as a man's?"

"Tell it to him again!" cried Aunt Sally.

"Don't she speak the truth. . . ."

"Glory be, glory be . . ."

Women called out from all directions.

"I know how hard it is for you women," Mother Jones continued, "for I too have suffered. And I know how hard it is for you men. Mining at its best is wretched work—breathing coal dust and damp air, never seeing sunlight. Never knowing when the roof might collapse, crushing your back and legs or burying you alive. Standing in sulphur water that eats through your shoes and brings sores to your flesh. Swinging your pick and ax where the roofs are so low you have to stoop over until your back aches too much to ever straighten up. A lifetime of working fourteen hours a day and nothing to show for it."

All around Rosie and Mary women were sighing and nodding their heads in agreement. Some women were crying.

Mother Jones raised her arms. "I can't argue with Jack about how bad things are. This strike has been going on for four months, and the company hasn't budged. Some of you have been thrown out of your houses. There's little or no money to buy food. No one thought it would last this long. I understand why you think going back to work is the only choice."

"Why shouldn't we?" a voice cried out.

"Because if you do," Mother Jones replied, "things will never change! Let's look at the facts. You're on strike because you're earning the same money today as you earned seven years ago. Seven years is a long time to go without a pay raise."

Her pointed finger swung in an arc around the field. "If you go back to work now, it will be for the same low wages and long hours." She lowered her voice to almost a whisper. Rosie and Mary leaned forward so as not to miss a word. "You'll die in the mines. Your sons will die in the mines and so will your grandsons. And you won't even have enough money to bury them.

"You've got to stick together. If your brothers in other mines can stay out, *you* can stay out. If they can go hungry, *you* can go

hungry. If their children can go hungry, *your* children can go hungry." Rosie squeezed Mary's hand.

Mother Jones stretched out her arms again, her voice soaring like the preacher's on Sunday. "You've got to rise and pledge to stick to your brothers until this strike is won."

Rosie's father and mother rose. Then Aunt Sally. Rosie's brother Henry stood up and began clapping and stamping his feet. Rosie and Mary jumped up and down, striking their hands together as fast and as hard as they could. One by one, other men, their wives and children by their sides, stood up. The clapping swelled until it was deafening.

Mother Jones wasn't finished yet. "At five o'clock tomorrow morning," she yelled, "I want every woman to meet me at the bottom of the hill. You men stay home and take care of the children for a change. We'll take care of any man who dares to go back to work. I want every woman to come and bring a mop, a broom, or a dishpan. Our army will make sure that no one goes into the mines." She dropped her arms and began to sing,

> "*Bring the good old bugle, boys!*
> *We'll sing another song;*
> *Sing it with a spirit*
> *That will start the world along. . . .*"

The crowd joined in, and the meeting ended in a burst of song.

Rosie's mother hugged her. "That's why mine owners call Mother Jones the most dangerous woman in America," she said.

She sure can talk, Rosie thought, but the part about the brooms and mops and the army, that was crazy.

"I must compliment you ladies." Mother Jones walked up to them. "You sure did teach those men something about courage." She took Aunt Sally's hand. "Not easy standing up like that in front of everyone, defying your husband."

"Sure wasn't," Aunt Sally said softly.

"I was stopped by the sheriff before coming to this meeting," Mother Jones continued. "He told me he had a warrant, and if I went anywhere near those mines, he'd have me arrested. Now I don't mind being arrested." She grinned. "Some of the most patriotic Americans I know have fought for justice and ended up in jail. But I don't think it would be good strategy right now to end up in jail. So one of you ladies will have to lead the army tomorrow."

"Louann had better do it," Aunt Sally said. "Jack didn't stand with the rest of us. I may have my hands full tomorrow morning with him."

"I'll gladly do it," said Rosie's mother.

"Then it's settled," Mother Jones said. "Now get your daughters home so they can get some sleep and march with us tomorrow."

October 16, 1899

It was still dark outside, but Rosie's mother was rushing around the house, banging a hammer on an old tin dishpan. "Hurry up, darlin'! Hurry up, and don't forget the broom." Rosie jumped out of bed. She dressed hurriedly, grabbed her broom and raced after her mother.

A crowd of women was gathering at the bottom of the hill that led to the mines. Rosie looked around for Mary but couldn't find her. She noticed a few of the older girls from school standing with their mothers.

Mother Jones's voice boomed as she made her way through the crowd. "How you doing? Right glad to see you. You sure look dangerous."

Rosie counted the women. Twenty. Thirty. Forty. Fifty. Six—

"Rosie!"

Rosie turned around and hugged her cousin. "Mary! Where have you been? I've been looking for you. Isn't it great? There must be at least a hundred women here. It really is like an army, isn't it?"

Mary pulled her cousin away from the crowd. "Pa left the house before anybody was up," she whispered. "He went back to work."

"I don't believe you," Rosie yelled.

"Shh! Ma told us she won't let him in the house as long as he's a scab. I never saw her so mad. Rosie, I'm scared."

"Now why are you two huddling over here?" The warmth in Mother Jones's voice surprised them. "Aren't you two girls the Wilson daughters?"

"We sure are," Rosie said proudly. Mary looked down at the ground.

"Glad to have you marching with us." She patted Mary on the shoulder. "Right good cymbal," she said, looking at Mary's dishpan. "The scabs'll sure hear you coming." She pulled out a red cloth from her dress pocket and handed it to Rosie. "Tie this to your broom. Then the scabs will see you coming."

"Mother Jones," Rosie's mother said, "I think everyone who's coming is here."

"Then let's get moving." Mother Jones turned to the crowd. "Friends, I can't go with you to the mines," she said. "I've been threatened with arrest if I do. But you don't need me. Louann Wilson will lead the army. Don't be afraid of anyone. When you see those scabs, hammer and howl. Hammer and howl. Use your mops, use your brooms and chase those men away."

Rosie's mother beat on her dishpan. "Fall in!" she cried. The women lined up behind her.

"Let's go," Rosie said to Mary, lifting her banner as high as she could.

"We will never retreat!" chanted Rosie's mother.

"We will never retreat!" cried Rosie.

"We will never retreat!" shouted Mary.

"We will never retreat." The women picked up the refrain and followed Rosie's mother along the creek and up the steep hill that led to the mines.

from
It's Our World, Too!
by Phillip Hoose

James Ale

When he was nine, James Ale saw his friend get hit by a car when they were playing ball in a crowded street. It made him wonder, Why should they have to play in the street when kids in the rich part of town had parks? The more he thought, the madder he got. Finally, James Ale took on town hall.

James Ale cried out as his friend Bobby Adams settled into position to catch the ball. Bobby was concentrating so hard that he didn't hear the white Thunderbird as it tore around the corner, heading toward him. He was on the ground, his leg bent in pain, before he even knew what happened.

James and his friends live in Davie, Florida, on the edge of the Everglades. Davie is really two towns. The western part is where rich people from Miami build ranches and keep their horses. The eastern part, where James and Bobby live, is a neighborhood of small trailers and condominiums on tiny lots.

At the time Bobby Adams was hit by the car, their neighborhood was full of children who had no place to play but in the street. At night, kids crawled around on Dumpsters left in front of construction sites. The nearest park was across a highway. You took your life in your hands every time you tried to get there. James's parents wouldn't let him even try.

As the sound of Bobby's ambulance faded into the distance, James walked slowly home. He was angry. Bobby wouldn't have gotten hurt if they had a park to play in. But officials never spent any money in this part of town.

James looked over at a small worn field right behind the water plant. That would be a perfect place for a park. There could be a playground at one end for the little kids and a basketball court at the other end. And some lights. Everyone would use it.

In that moment, James decided to make it happen. He'd organize the kids, and they'd beat down the mayor's door. They'd call themselves Children for Davie. So what if he was only nine?

That evening, James asked his dad for advice. As president of the local condominium association, John Ale was always going off to the town council meetings. If anyone would know how to pressure Davie's government, his dad would.

John Ale listened carefully to his son's idea before speaking. "You'll have to know exactly what you want and be able to prove that it's important. Playground equipment will cost money, and people ask the mayor and the town council for money every day," he said. "Everyone thinks their project is the most important thing in the world, and there's only so much tax money to go around."

Father and son sat together in silence. "But you can do it," Mr. Ale said. "More than anything, you'll have to be persistent. You can't quit."

Preparing for Action

James decided to start at the top. The next day, he telephoned the mayor.

"Mayor Kovac's office," said a pleasant voice.

"May I talk to the mayor?"

"She's not in. May I take a message?"

James left his name and telephone number. A few hours later, the mayor called him back. "I told her what had happened to Bobby Adams and said we needed a park in our neighborhood," James recalls. "I could tell she wasn't paying much attention. She seemed to be in a hurry. All she said was that she'd look into it and call me back.

"A while later she did. She said once there had been a park in our area and it had been vandalized. It was like we had blown our only chance. Then she didn't say anything. Finally I just said, 'Well, I think we need a park,' and we hung up. I felt discouraged. She treated me like a kid. I had to get her to pay attention."

James went to his room, flicked on his computer, and typed *Children for Davie* in bold print at the top of the screen. Below that, he typed out a petition calling for a new park. "Please sign this if you think that it would be better for our neighborhood if there were a park," it concluded. Beneath that he put blanks for signatures.

He printed it out, snapped it onto a clipboard, and went outside to try to get kids to sign it. They squinted at his petition, then looked at him as if he were crazy.

"Sure, man, *you're* gonna get us a park."

"Well, don't you think we need one? Look what happened to Bobby."

"Yeah, we need one, but who's gonna listen to *you*?"

"Not just me. We'll all go. She'll have to listen to all of us."

"You're outa your mind." They were starting to drift away.

"Well, just sign it if you're for it, okay?"

James got fifty kids to sign, but no one would go with him to see the mayor, not even Bobby Adams, who by now was back from the hospital and recovering from a broken leg.

James called the mayor again, this time asking for an appointment to talk about the park in person. She said yes. James prepared carefully for that meeting. Above all, he needed to be taken seriously.

Here's what he did:

- He gathered more signatures on his petition.

- He took a map of Davie and outlined the site where he wanted the park, so the mayor would know just where it should be.

- He typed out a letter on his Children for Davie stationery to leave with the mayor, listing the reasons why the park should be built and stating exactly what the town should provide: swings, a slide, monkey bars, a basketball court, and lights.

- He made up some business cards on his computer. They said, "James Ale, President, Children for Davie."

On the afternoon of the meeting, James put on his red suit jacket, a red shirt, and gray pants and squeezed into his hard black shoes. He combed his hair carefully. "When the time came for my mom to pick me up and drive me over there, I was ready."

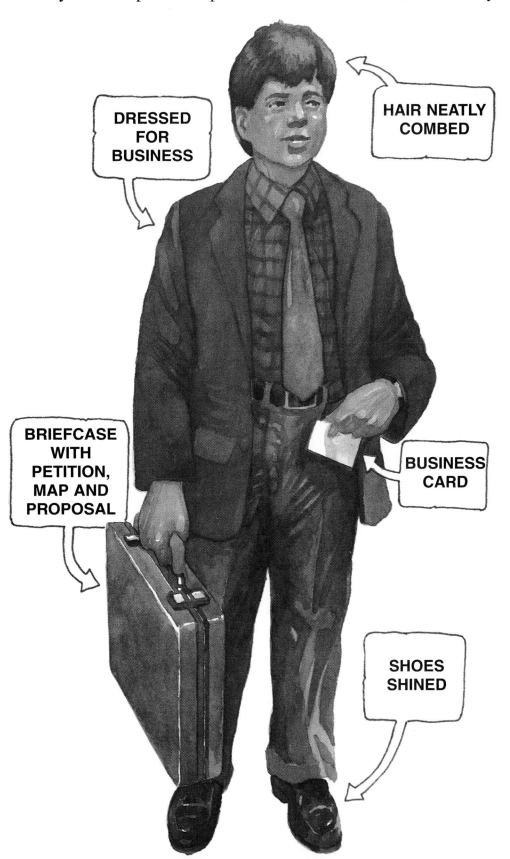

"It Should Be Here."

Mayor Joan Kovac had expected James Ale to be a child who maybe wanted to tell his friends he had met the mayor in person. But the boy who walked through the door had business on his mind. "He came in with a briefcase," she recalls. "And then he handed me a business card."

Looking directly at her, James told the mayor that his neighborhood was unsafe for kids. They had no place to play. They needed a park. It would help the town, he said, because it would save lives. The crime rate would go down because kids would have something to do. Mayor Kovac was leaning forward, looking right at him and listening carefully. When he finished, she got up and walked around her desk to a map of Davie. She pointed to three dots, clustered together on the west side of town.

CHILDREN FOR DAVIE

JAMES ALE
President   792-7758

"We're building three new parks right now, James," she said. "Can't your parents take you to one of them?"

"No," said James. "My parents both work. So do everyone else's around me. Those parks are a long way from us. We need a place of our own."

The mayor looked at the map again. "But there's no empty land where you live. Everything's all built up. Do you have a suggestion?"

James pulled the map from his briefcase and spread it on the mayor's desk. "It should be here," he said, pointing to the square he had drawn. "Behind the water plant. It's the right place. Look at this petition from the kids in the neighborhood. Everyone agrees."

Mayor Kovac had no choice but to respect him. He wasn't criticizing her or blaming the town. He had come to her with a plan. He was representing a group, and he wanted her support. She had to consider his proposal.

"Well," she said at last, "let me talk to some people in the Parks Department. We'll have to visit the site. I can't make any promises now, but I can promise I won't just put you off."

James got up and extended his hand, smiling. He pointed to his card on her desk. "My phone number is right here," he said. "I look forward to hearing from you."

"We're Going to Build That Kid a Park."

One Saturday morning a few weeks later, James met the mayor and the town administrator behind the water tower. James had been studying up on how Davie's government worked. The mayor and the town administrator were Davie's two most important officials. Along with the town attorney and the five members of the town council, they made the big decisions on how to run Davie's business. The town administrator did most of the detailed, day-to-day business.

James had gone to meet with him, too. He was a nice enough man—he had even given James tickets to a wrestling meet—but he didn't seem very interested in the park. Still, he had agreed to visit the site. Now James had the town's two most important people together right where he wanted them. This was his chance.

First James pointed to the spot where Bobby Adams had been hit. Several kids were running around. They had to agree that it would be hard for a turning car to see them.

Then James walked them around the small field. "This is the perfect place for us," James said. The administrator frowned. The lot was too small for a park, he said. He advised James to be patient. Someday the town would tear down a couple of houses and build the kids a real park.

"We don't want to wait for a bigger park," James said flatly. "We need this park, here and now. This is the right place. It will get used. You already own the land, and we're just talking about playground equipment. We're not asking for much." He could see the man's mind was closed.

If they thought James Ale would go away, they were wrong. He waited a few days for an answer, and when none came, he tried even harder. Nearly every day after school, he wrote brief, carefully worded letters to town officials. He also sent them updated copies of his ever-growing petition.

One night he called the secretary assigned to the town council and asked if, representing Children for Davie, he could speak briefly to the council members at Wednesday night's meeting.

"Are you a voter?" the secretary asked.

"Well, no, but I—"

"Then the answer is no," she said firmly.

James turned up the heat. He called the reporter for a Miami newspaper assigned to Davie and offered him the story of a young boy taking on town hall for the kids in his neighborhood. The reporter accepted, and a story soon appeared in the newspaper. James sent a copy to town officials.

Every few days, he called Mayor Kovac and asked her for a progress report. He was always polite. Did she need any more information? Was there anything he could do to help?

Finally his work paid off. One evening after school, James was surprised to receive a call from the town council's secretary inviting him to a council meeting. The next Wednesday evening, Mayor Kovac announced the creation of a new park. Asking him to stand, she introduced James by saying, "This boy could teach a lot of adults I know a few things about lobbying town government."

Mayor Kovac says that the small area that everyone in Davie now calls James Ale Park has become the most popular playground site in Davie. "I drive by it, and there are never fewer than thirty kids there," she says. "The parks we built in the richer parts of town are barely used. James was right."

The kids in the neighborhood thought it was a miracle that a nine-year-old boy actually got his town to spend five thousand dollars to build a park for them. But it wasn't a miracle. He simply used tried-and-true lobbying techniques.

"This kid could teach a lot of adults I know how to lobby elected officials. He just didn't give up."
—Mayor Joan Kovac, Davie, Florida

In Mayor Kovac's words:

- James went right to the person who had power—me, in this case—and got to know me. It was smart, because lobbying is partly personal. I like James.

- He came with a very specific plan. He had it in writing so that I could show it to people.

- His petition showed that he was representing other children.

- He was able to say, in a very few words, why that park was needed. And I could tell he really believed in it.

- He didn't come with a budget—probably he should have—but he knew what he wanted at the park. That made it easy for me to figure out the cost.

- He was always available to meet officials at the site. He provided information that we needed. He was on time.

- He was respectful. He kept pressure on us without being obnoxious or turning us off. And he listened to me.

- He was persistent. That's the most important thing of all. He just never gave up. I don't think he ever would have.

- One other thing. He paid me back, and in the right way. When my campaign for reelection came up, James called and asked if he could help. He went door-to-door asking people to vote for me. I mean he really *blitzed* that neighborhood. He was an asset to me. During the campaign, I listed the creation of James Ale Park as one of my major accomplishments.

s honored

James Ale, 12, sits
Ale Park last week

Activist, 12, traveling to meet Soviet counte

By BETH DUFF SANDERS
Staff Writer

DAVIE — The road between Davie and Moscow is paved with good intentions. And James Ale, 12, helped to lay down the asphalt.

His yearlong effort to get the town of Davie to pave over a vacant lot and build a playground for children in his small, working-class neighborhood won him national recognition and a trip to the Soviet Union.

Ale leaves today for Vermont, where he

James Ale
peace-related projects.

will join 29 other young Americans who worked to improve their communities.

On Monday, the 30 youngsters, along with adult chaperones and translators, leave for the Soviet Union on a goodwill mission sponsored by an ice-cream company known for its socially conscious and

Ale said his classmates at Driftwood Middle School in Davie "don't believe me, that I'm really going. They think I'm just pulling their leg."

But going he is.

The first stop is Moscow, then on to Kiev and Leningrad.

"And you know what? I've heard such nice things about the Russians, I don't know why we'd ever want to hurt them," Ale said on Friday, between packing and getting a haircut. "I'm going to tell them what life is like in America."

When Ale was 9 he began a relentless

string of phone c
officials, demand
neighborhood chil
hang out on the st

"I was playing o
guy came around
these hot-rod Corve
over," he said. "So

A year later, Jar
cated at the end
Terrace.

Since then, he ha

SEE T

And what did James learn? "I learned a lot. People in government will tell a kid that they don't have time for little things like a park," James says. "But if you think about it, it really is a big thing. I had a good idea and I never gave up. Kids have rights, too. But we have to learn to use them."

Broward County

ark, but anyone can pla

ens of factors that go
decision to give nationw
thority, and it's studie
carefully." — MARK

Property owner
Pines Blvd. fac

Private property
week gave Pembrok
or Charles Flanagar
r e -
s p o n
s e
to a pro-
p o s a l
t h a t
they pay for imp
Pines Boulevard

The improv
could cost aro
would include
levard to six
go Road to
landscaped
areas, and
bicycle path
es and bus s

The may
city borr
assess lan
ern secti
of the i
made. T
back ov

How
the ma
agreed

Paul Hurschmann/SUN STAFF

on monkey bars at James
in Davie.

C.M. GUERRERO / Miami Herald

Looking as humble as a hero can be, James Ale, 9, accepts thanks from his pals
at a new Davie park.

permitting — giving quick ap-
proval for construction — is not
without safeguards.

"It's an intent to simplify the
process and expedite a decision,"
Evans said. "But there are doz-

by dense development.
They say the U.S. Army Corps

MENTOR

Suki Cheong

CHILDREN'S•EXPRESS
QUARTERLY

"It's Your Brain, Not Your Color"
Teenagers Discuss How Racism Affects Them

A Principal's Recipe For Racial Tolerance

Finding Solutions Without Fighting

Editor

This *editor* knows what the scoop is!

Since fourth grade, sixteen-year-old Suki Cheong has worked for *Children's Express*, an international news service run by kids. *Children's Express* has news bureaus in several states, and its weekly column appears in newspapers all over the country. The reporters, ages 8–13, and the editors, ages 14–18, write stories about issues such as health, education, and government. Now that Suki is an editor, she helps younger reporters get the scoop on lead stories.

PROFILE

Name: Suki Cheong

Job: student, Senior Editor/*Children's Express*

Education: Stuyvesant High School, New York City

Awards: Both a Peabody and an Emmy award for coverage of the 1988 Presidential elections

Role Model: Hillary Clinton

Favorite Newspaper Section: The Op-Ed pages

QUESTIONS
for Suki Cheong

Discover how Suki Cheong *writes about* issues from a kid's point of view.

Q What was your first job at *Children's Express?*

A I started out as a reporter at *Children's Express*. Right away, I was responsible for preparing questions and doing interviews.

Q What's your job now that you are an editor?

A It's not like a typical news editor's job. I don't just edit the story—my job is to guide the reporter. I research the subject that we're doing an article on, and gather together statistics and facts we might need. If it's an interview, I set up a time and place for the interview, then brief the reporter. After an interview, I help write the actual article. I also help organize projects, conferences, and roundtable discussions.

Q Who chooses the stories that go into *Children's Express?*

A Every month we have a meeting with all the kids in the bureau. We brainstorm and then vote on our ideas. Then the reporters decide which ones they want to work on.

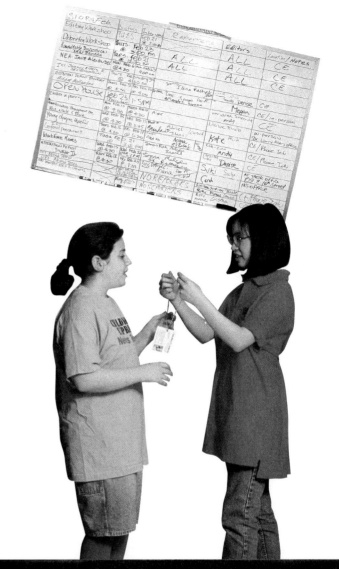

 What issues do you think are important to write about?

 Any issues that affect children are important, such as violence in schools and on the streets, education and health. The most interesting interview I ever did was with Miguel, a sixteen-year-old who lives in a violent neighborhood. I felt it was important for people to hear his story.

 Do you think that *Children's Express* can have an effect on your community and others?

 The purpose of *Children's Express* is to make sure that kids have a voice in their community. Maybe our stories don't always make an immediate difference. But they will make people think about an issue in a new way—from a kid's point of view.

Suki Cheong's
Tips for Young Reporters

1 Research the subject of your story or interview.

2 If it's an interview, prepare your questions ahead of time. Ask permission if you want to tape the interview.

3 Before you start writing, decide how you want to organize your story.

How to
Make a Public Service Announcement

How can you make information available to your community? One way is through a public service announcement on radio or television.

What's a public service announcement? Public service announcements give information to the community. They are broadcast free of charge by radio and TV stations. Have you ever listened to the radio and heard that your school is closed because of bad weather? That's a public service announcement! A public service announcement may also tell about a community event, such as a book fair or a fund drive.

Phone number or address for more information

AMERICAN RED CROSS ●●●●●●●●●●●●●●●●●●●●●●●●●●●●●●● **Name of the group involved**

Radio: 30

Live Announcer Script

●●●●●●● **Body of message**

Somewhere in the country…this very day…disaster struck. In fact, disaster strikes every single day. Which means every single night someone needs food, shelter, and a place to rest. You can make a difference. Please support the American Red Cross. Call 1-800-842-2200. Because every night is another night someone needs your help.

1 Choose a Topic

Brainstorm a list of real community issues or events for your public service announcement. Perhaps a group in your town plans to raise money for a new park, or maybe your school is putting on a play. Make a list of events and issues. Then pick the one that means the most to you.

TOOLS

- pencil and paper
- local newspapers
- posterboard and colored markers
- tape recorder (optional)

2 Organize Your Facts

Do research to learn more about the issue or event you chose. You can read the local newspaper, watch the local TV news, or talk to people in your community. Take notes on what you learn. When you're finished, see whether you can answer the "5 Ws": Who, What, When, Where, and Why. If you can't, you'll need to do some more research.

Support THE In-line Skating Park

3 Write a Script

Here's how to write a script for your public service announcement.

- Say that you are making a public service announcement.

- Tell the name of the group that is involved.

- State the reason for the announcement.

- If you are announcing an event, give the time and place that it will be held.

- Explain to the audience members how they can get more information.

- Try to use words that will catch your audience's attention.

Tips
- State your message in the fewest words possible.
- Use action verbs to make your announcement more interesting.
- Listen to radio and TV announcers to see how they sound.
- Practice saying your announcement before you present it.

4 Present Your Public Service Announcement

There are many ways to present your public service announcement. You can read it "live" to the class, or read it into a tape recorder and play the tape for the class. You might want to add music and sound effects to make the announcement more dramatic.

If You Are Using a Computer ...

Use the Record and Playback tools as you write your public service announcement on the computer. You also may want to create a public service announcement, using clip art and borders, to appear in a newspaper.

THINK

Why are public service announcements an important service for the community?

Suki Cheong
Editor ▶

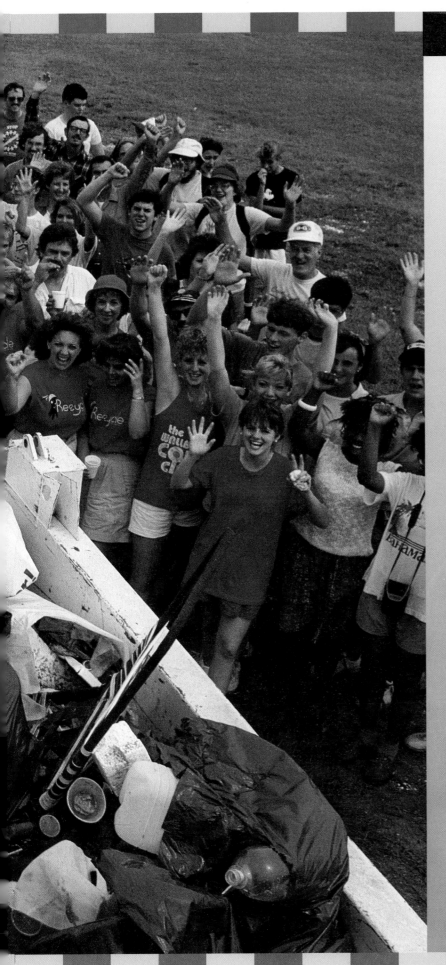

It takes leadership and an organized effort to reach our goals.

Ideas in Action

Find out how Jackie Robinson became the first African American to play major league baseball.

Follow a father and son on their mission to save Mexico's last rain forest. Then read letters from kids in China who want to help save the environment.

PROJECT

Make your opinion known—write a letter to the editor.

Teammates

Jackie Robinson

"Pee Wee" Reese

by Peter Golenbock
illustrated by **Paul Bacon**

AWARD WINNING Book

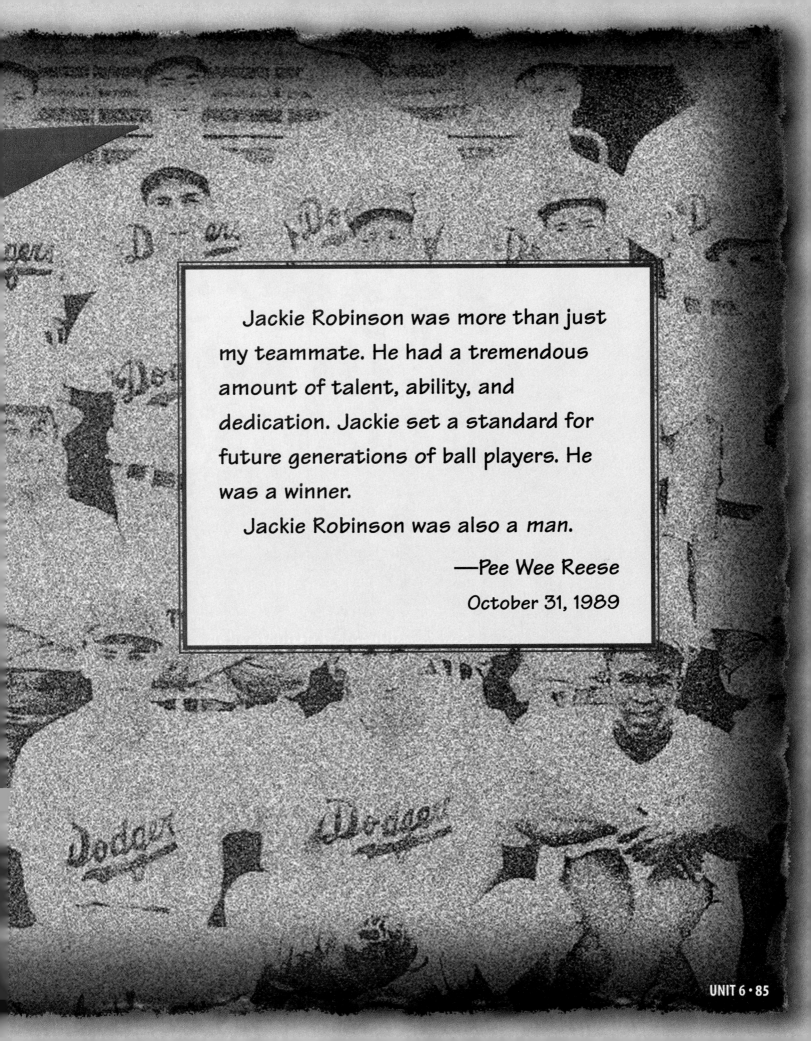

Jackie Robinson was more than just my teammate. He had a tremendous amount of talent, ability, and dedication. Jackie set a standard for future generations of ball players. He was a winner.

Jackie Robinson was also a *man*.

—Pee Wee Reese

October 31, 1989

Once upon a time in America, when automobiles were black and looked like tanks and laundry was white and hung on clotheslines to dry, there were two wonderful baseball leagues that no longer exist. They were called the Negro Leagues.

The Negro Leagues had extraordinary players, and adoring fans came to see them wherever they played. They were heroes, but players in the Negro Leagues didn't make much money and their lives on the road were hard.

SATCHEL PAIGE

Laws against segregation didn't exist in the 1940s. In many places in this country, black people were not allowed to go to the same schools and churches as white people. They couldn't sit in the front of a bus or trolley car. They couldn't drink from the same drinking fountains that white people drank from.

Back then, many hotels didn't rent rooms to black people, so the Negro League players slept in their cars. Many towns had no restaurants that would serve them, so they often had to eat meals that they could buy and carry with them.

WHITE ONLY

Life was very different for the players in the Major Leagues. They were the leagues for white players. Compared to the Negro League players, white players were very well paid. They stayed in good hotels and ate in fine restaurants. Their pictures were put on baseball cards and the best players became famous all over the world.

Many Americans knew that racial prejudice was wrong, but few dared to challenge openly the way things were. And many people were apathetic about racial problems. Some feared that it could be dangerous to object. Vigilante groups, like the Ku Klux Klan, reacted violently against those who tried to change the way blacks were treated.

The general manager of the Brooklyn Dodgers baseball team was a man by the name of Branch Rickey. He was not afraid of change. He wanted to treat the Dodger fans to the best players he could find, regardless of the color of their skin. He thought segregation was

BABE RUTH

"TED" WILLIAMS

unfair and wanted to give everyone, regardless of race or creed, an opportunity to compete equally on ballfields across America.

To do this, the Dodgers needed one special man.

Branch Rickey launched a search for him. He was looking for a star player in the Negro Leagues who would be able to compete successfully despite threats on his life or attempts to injure him. He would have to possess the self-control not to fight back when opposing players tried to intimidate or hurt him. If this man disgraced himself on the field, Rickey knew, his opponents would use it as an excuse to keep blacks out of Major League baseball for many more years.

Rickey thought Jackie Robinson might be just the man.

Jackie rode the train to Brooklyn to meet Mr. Rickey. When Mr. Rickey told him, "I want a man with the courage not to fight back," Jackie Robinson replied, "If you take this gamble, I will do my best to perform." They shook hands. Branch Rickey and Jackie Robinson were starting on what would be known in history as "the great experiment."

At spring training with the Dodgers, Jackie was mobbed by blacks, young and old, as if he were a savior. He was the first black player to try out for a Major League team. If he succeeded, they knew, others would follow.

Initially, life with the Dodgers was for Jackie a series of humiliations. The players on his team who came from the South, men who had been taught to avoid black people since childhood, moved to another table whenever he sat down next to them. Many opposing players were cruel to him, calling him nasty names from their dugouts. A few tried to hurt him with their spiked shoes. Pitchers aimed at his head. And he received threats on his life, both from individuals and from organizations like the Ku Klux Klan.

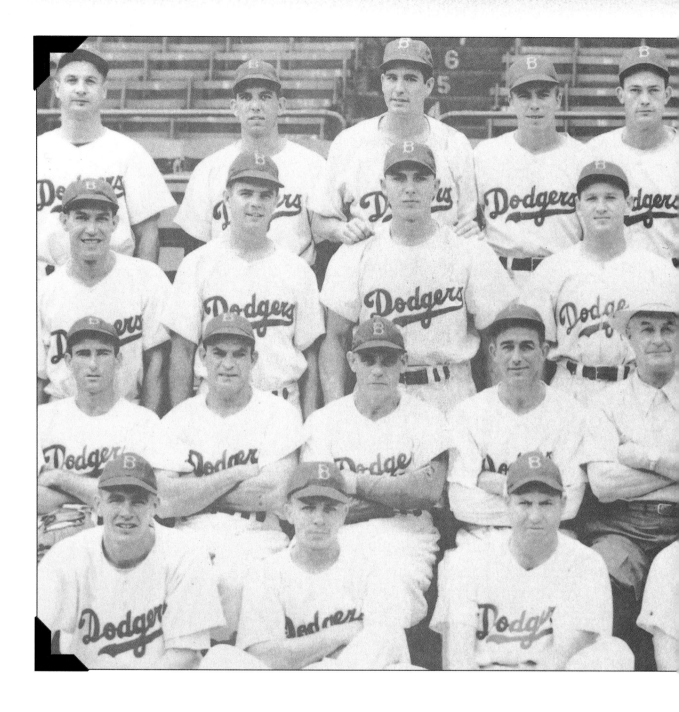

Despite all the difficulties, Jackie Robinson didn't give up.
He made the Brooklyn Dodgers team.

But making the Dodgers was only the beginning. Jackie
had to face abuse and hostility throughout the season, from

April through September. His worst pain was inside. Often he felt very alone. On the road he had to live by himself, because only the white players were allowed in the hotels in towns where the team played.

The whole time Pee Wee Reese, the Dodger shortstop, was growing up in Louisville, Kentucky, he had rarely even seen a black person, unless it was in the back of a bus. Most of his friends and relatives hated the idea of his playing on the same field as a black man. In addition, Pee Wee Reese had more to lose than the other players when Jackie joined the team.

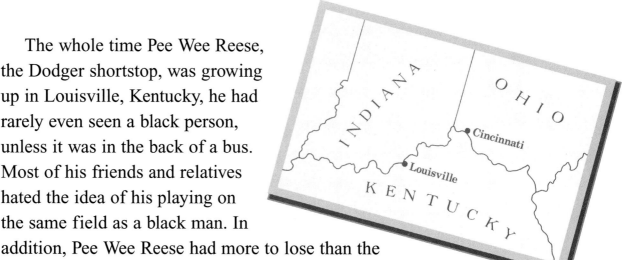

Jackie had been a shortstop, and everyone thought that Jackie would take Pee Wee's job. Lesser men might have felt anger toward Jackie, but Pee Wee was different. He told himself, "If he's good enough to take my job, he deserves it."

When his Southern teammates circulated a petition to throw Jackie off the team and asked him to sign it, Pee Wee responded, "I don't care if this man is black, blue, or striped"— and refused to sign. "He can play and he can help us win," he told the others. "That's what counts."

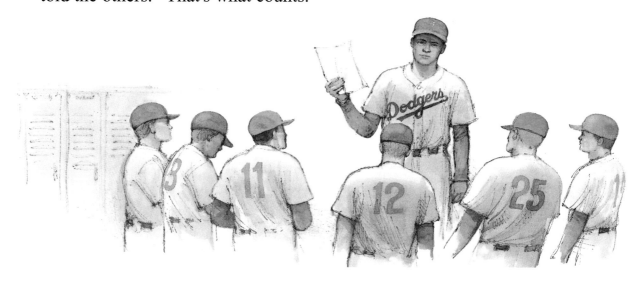

CROSLEY FIELD

Very early in the season, the Dodgers traveled west to Ohio to play the Cincinnati Reds. Cincinnati is near Pee Wee's hometown of Louisville.

The Reds played in a small ballpark where the fans sat close to the field. The players could almost feel the breath of the fans on the backs of their necks. Many who came that day screamed terrible, hateful things at Jackie when the Dodgers were on the field.

More than anything else, Pee Wee Reese believed in doing what was right. When he heard the fans yelling at Jackie, Pee Wee decided to take a stand.

With his head high, Pee Wee walked directly from his shortstop position to where Jackie was playing first base. The taunts and shouting of the fans were ringing in Pee Wee's ears. It saddened him, because he knew it could have been his friends and neighbors. Pee Wee's legs felt heavy, but he knew what he had to do.

As he walked toward Jackie wearing the gray Dodger uniform, he looked into his teammate's bold, pained eyes. The first baseman had done nothing to

provoke the hostility except that he sought to be treated as an equal. Jackie was grim with anger. Pee Wee smiled broadly as he reached Jackie. Jackie smiled back.

Stopping beside Jackie, Pee Wee put his arm around Jackie's shoulders. An audible gasp rose up from the crowd when they saw what Pee Wee had done. Then there was silence.

Outlined on a sea of green grass stood these two great athletes, one black, one white, both wearing the same team uniform.

"I am standing by him," Pee Wee Reese said to the world. "This man is my teammate."

from

Save My Rainforest

by Monica Zak
illustrated by Bengt-Arne Runnerström
English version by Nancy Schimmel

*Omar Castillo lives in Mexico City. His
grandfather has told him about the last rainforest in
Mexico, and Omar dreams of visiting it someday.
One evening while watching the news on TV, Omar
learns about the destruction of the rainforest. He
convinces his father that they must take action. They
decide to walk to save the rainforest.*

Early one morning Omar and his father start walking. At first Omar is smiling and singing. On the road at last! And tonight, for the first time in his life, he will sleep in a tent.

For hours and hours they walk on the hot pavement. Finally, they leave the dirty yellow air of the city for the clear, clean air of the countryside. But Omar is too tired to notice. Then his feet begin to hurt. He goes a good ways before he says anything. When he does, his father stops and takes Omar's shoes off. "You have blisters. I'll put a bandage on . . . there. Now we can get started again."

"But Papa, I'm too tired. I can't go on."

"I'm tired too," says his father, "but try to go a little farther. I'll buy us a cool drink at the next store." They find a fruit stand where a woman with long braids sells them tall glasses of pineapple drink.

She looks at them curiously and finally asks, "What does your banner say? I can't read."

Omar revives at once. "This side says 'Let's protect the rainforest' and the other side says 'Walk—Mexico City—Tuxtla Gutiérrez.' Tuxtla's a long way south of here, but that's where we decided to go, to see the governor of the state of Chiapas, where the rainforest is. He is responsible for taking

CAMINATA MEXICO DF TUXTLA GTEZ

care of it. We need to tell him to save the rainforest so there will still be a rainforest in Mexico for us children when we grow up."

"You must be sent from heaven!" she says.

Omar's father smiles. "No, he's just a regular kid. All kids have good ideas, but usually people don't listen to them. It never made any difference to me that they were destroying the rainforest and the animals, but when I thought about what my son said, I realized that he knew what he was talking about. That's why I decided to come with him."

Another day, the sun beats down through the thin mountain air. This time it is Omar's father who has blisters. He calls, "Must you walk so fast, Omar?"

After walking more than a week, they come down out of the mountains. They can see banana plantations now, and *mango* trees. They camp by the side of the road.

Omar lies in the tent and listens. The night before, he heard coyotes howling near the tent: ah-ooo, ah-ooo, ah-ooo. He was afraid. Now he listens to the murmuring leaves. *What if a snake should get into the tent? What if robbers attack us?* he thinks. An enormous truck rumbles past and shakes the tent. *What if the driver fell asleep and . . .*

"Omar, are you awake?" his father asks.

"Mm-hm," answers Omar. "I can't sleep."

"Well," says Omar's father, "we really had a tough day. Heat, no shade, and traffic. Now it's pleasant. We won't be cold tonight."

"No," says Omar, smiling. "Remember the first night in the tent? I thought it would be wonderful, camping, but then the rain started . . ."

"Yes," says his father, "and the water came in. At three in the morning! Remember how good that hot *pozole* tasted after we walked in the dark and cold?"

"Papa, how many more days do we have to walk?"

"I thought it would take fifteen or twenty days, but it will take much longer. I don't want to disappoint you, but I don't believe we can go on."

"But why?" asks Omar, astounded.

"We are running out of money."

They decide to keep going.

"We will have to beg for food," says Omar.

They go into a restaurant and Omar's father explains to the owner why they are walking. "We have no more money," Omar's father says, "and my son is awfully hungry." The owner turns them out without giving them even a glass of water. But then a woman sitting outside a little hut motions them in, makes a fresh pot of coffee, and serves them coffee and bread. It goes like that. Some days people give them food, but often they have to walk the whole day without eating anything. Those days are hard.

When Omar sees boys playing soccer, he stops and watches with envy, but they never ask him to play. Sometimes there are things to look at in the road: a huge scorpion or snakes run over by cars. But more often, walking is boring. Omar throws rocks at fenceposts, thinking *Why didn't I bring anything to play with?* Then somebody who hears he is going

to the rainforest gives him a toy Tarzan. He passes the time pretending Tarzan is in the rainforest, swinging from vines.

People warn them not to take the shortest way to Tuxtla, the road that goes through poor villages. "They'll attack you and rob you. It's too dangerous!" But Omar and his father take that road anyway, because it is 125 miles shorter. At first they are a little afraid, but no one attacks them. In fact, women and children come out and give them oranges and *tortilla* chips.

On the morning of their twenty-fifth day of traveling, Omar's father wakes him with "Las Mananitas" on his harmonica. Omar had forgotten—today he is nine! His father gives him a big hug and kiss, but Omar can see that he is sad—there is no money for birthday presents. Then, in the afternoon, they come to a little village where the people have already heard about their walk to save the rainforest. When they find out it is Omar's birthday, a woman bakes him a cake and invites all the neighbors for a real *fiesta de cumpleaños.* The house is full of people. And the cake! It is enormous, and chocolate, and has nine candles.

Everyone says, "Omar, blow out the candles!" What a lucky day! Omar grins whipped cream and chocolate from ear to ear.

A few days later they stop in a little town to eat in a restaurant. An announcer comes on television to say there has been a terrible earthquake in Mexico City.

They see a picture of a big pile of rubble and hear that it is the hospital where Omar's grandmother works! Omar starts to cry. His father has tears in his eyes. No one can reach Mexico City by telephone

because the lines are out. Then a ham radio operator in the town promises he will help them get news.

After four days of waiting, the radio operator says, "Your *abuela* is alive, Omar. She wasn't in the hospital when the earthquake came. Your mother is well. She sends you kisses and says your house wasn't hurt at all. She wishes you a safe journey."

And now they can continue.

After thirty-nine days of walking, Omar and his father come to Tuxtla Gutiérrez. They have travelled 870 miles and they are tired. They have to wait the whole day outside the governor's office, but finally the moment comes that Omar has been hoping for.

His heart beats loudly as he faces the governor and says, "Save my rainforest and stop the hunting of the rainforest animals for the next twenty years." The governor pats Omar on the head and says there is nothing to worry about.

Omar still worries. *He is treating me like a kid,* he thinks. *He won't do anything.*

But Omar does get to see a rainforest. When Tuxtla was built, a piece of the rainforest was left as a park. At first, Omar is disappointed in the rainforest, too. There aren't lots of strange animals running around in plain sight. Just gigantic trees and a clean wet smell.

Omar stands quietly for a long time in the deep green light amid the huge trunks, listening to all the birds singing high above in the canopy of leaves. Then he knows that being in a real rainforest at last is worth the trouble of walking 870 miles.

Omar and his father meet the zoologist, Don Miguel, who takes care of the park. Don Miguel explains, "They cut some of the trees for lumber, but mostly they are cutting the forest, and even burning some of the trees, to clear land to graze cattle. Every time somebody eats a hamburger, the people who cut the rainforest get more money.

"You saw how dry the land is around Tuxtla. It's dry because the rainforest is gone. Cutting down the forest changes the climate. Now this little piece of rainforest has to be irrigated to preserve it. It's a rainforest without rain!"

Omar also learns that medicines come from the rainforest plants. More medicines could be found if the rainforests were left standing.

"I am old and tired," says Don Miguel to Omar's father. "I have been fighting all my life to save the rainforest. I don't have the strength to go on. So I am happy to know there are people like this boy. It gives me hope."

When Omar hears Don Miguel say this, he knows he can't give up. *I have to talk to the President,* he thinks. *After all, he is the one responsible for the whole country.*

When they get home, Omar goes to see the President. But it doesn't matter that he walked all the way to Tuxtla Gutiérrez to save the rainforest. The President will not see him.

So Omar and his father set up the little red tent under the President's balcony. Immediately a crowd gathers.

"Are you crazy?" they ask. "Why are you camping in the *Zocalo*?"

"Because I want to talk to the President," explains Omar, "and I won't leave until he listens to what I have to say."

All the cold December day, he marches around the huge plaza with his banner. By night, Omar's teeth are chattering, and still the President has not come out.

The next day, the newspapers run a story about Omar. More people come to see him.

Drivers give him the thumbs-up sign or call out to him, "*Arriba*, Omar! We're with you! Save the rainforest!"

That night, people Omar and his father don't even know come to guard them as they sleep.

Children come to play with Omar. They listen to the story of his walk. They make paper signs and start parading about the *Zocalo* with him.

"We will save the rainforest!" they shout at the top of their lungs. For four days.

Finally, Omar is so tired that he stops under the President's balcony and yells, "Señor Presidente! I am hungry and cold. Please let me come in. Señor Presidente, if you have children, think about them." No one appears on the balcony. Omar starts walking again. Two hundred times around the *Zocalo*. Then a man comes to tell Omar that the President wants to talk to him.

"Papa! It's happened!" shouts Omar, running to give his father a big hug. The children cheer as Omar goes into the palace. He knows he doesn't have much time so he just says the most important thing. He asks the President to save the last great rainforest of the country so it can be left to the children of Mexico as their inheritance.

The President promises Omar that in one year, the rainforest cutting will stop and nobody will be allowed to capture the rainforest birds and animals to sell them for pets.

Omar comes out of the presidential palace walking on air.

For a while, Omar is content, thinking that the President will save the rainforest.

A year later Omar goes to the Sonora Market in the center of the city. He looks at the beautiful toys, but he is really there to see the animals. In the corner of the huge marketplace where they sell pets, he finds a *toucan* in a cage.

The President had promised that no more rainforest creatures would be caught and sold, but he has broken his promise. Omar knows they are still cutting down trees, too. "I promise to keep working to save your home," Omar says to the *toucan*, "and I will keep *my* promise."

GLOSSARY

abuela—grandmother

arriba—hurray

fiesta de cumpleaños—birthday party

mango—tropical fruit

pozole—hominy soup

tortillas—corn or wheat flat bread

toucan—tropical bird

Zocalo—main square or plaza

The 870-mile route that Omar and his father walked

Did you enjoy this story of the boy who wanted to save the rainforest? Well, it isn't a story. I am Omar Castillo. Now I am eleven; all that you read in this book happened when I was eight and nine.

I was very young then. I thought I had to do everything myself. I thought it would be enough to go and talk to the grown-ups who have the power to make decisions. I thought it would be enough just to say "Save my rainforest." Now I know this is not the way it works.

When I saw that they would keep destroying the rainforest, I went by bicycle to various states of Mexico. I asked the governors to write to the President asking him to protect the forests, but few of them agreed.

This showed me that I will not be able to save the rainforest by myself. It will take many of us to do that.

Now I have talked to many children in Mexico and I know that they think as I do: all children want a rainforest to be there when we grow up. And all the children I have talked to are as determined as I am. If the grown-ups don't stop cutting the Lacandon Rainforest, we will all have to go there; hundreds of thousands of children will make a chain that will surround the rainforest. And we will not move until they stop logging!

from

Dear

How Children Around the World Feel About Our Environment

edited by Lannis Temple

Dear World,

When I have time, I go into the forest and sit under a big tree. Then if I sit there for several hours without moving, without speaking, the animals start to come out. After a while, they're not afraid of me. Perhaps they think I'm a rock. If I'm very patient, sometimes small animals come right up to me. When that happens, I feel very happy because I know nature won't hurt me. Nature is like my second mother, whenever I need her she will help me.

But now many people are starting to go into the forest. They camp there, eat there, but when they go they leave all their rubbish behind them. Very unhealthy! How can they be so thoughtless? After they've left, the animals come back. They might eat a cardboard box, a plastic bag and then that bag might stick in their throat, so they can't get rid of it. Then they'd die. Really terrible!

I hope people will wake up. I want to tell the people of the world if they don't hurry up and protect nature, in a few years there won't be any nature.

Your friend,
Pu Lan
Age 13

你的朋友： 浦兰 13岁

World

Dear Natural World,

How are you? I like you very much. You are so changeable, so beautiful, so full of character. From the time when I was born, I have loved you and everything about you.

I love climbing mountains, reaching the top, gazing out in every direction, all worries left behind. This is why I find you fascinating.

On the days when I am sad, you seem to know it. Through a crack in my window, a gentle breeze blows mischievously against my face, reminding me of your beauty.

Sometimes in the morning, the fog is very thick. Then you change and sunlight floods in every direction. While I'm not looking, you change again to darkness and there is a big storm.

But sometimes I see men in the forest carelessly cutting down trees. Sometimes I see men pouring filthy water into the river. Again you are polluted.

I hope in the future we people can cooperate with you. We will plant more trees, we will no longer pollute you.

Hoping you become more beautiful.

Wang Lin

Age 12

王琳 女)

How to

Create an Op-Ed Page

State *your* **opinion** in a letter to the *editor*.

Many newspapers have an Op-Ed page. Editorials and letters to the editor appear on this page. Editorials are articles in which the newspaper's editors give their opinions. The letters are from readers, giving their opinions. Many different kinds of issues are discussed on the Op-Ed page.

Temple edges
Will meet UMass in Atlantic 10 c

The Pr

New Jersey Edition   b

Concerns deepen about the dollar

The decline against other currencies continues. "Everyone seems to wan currencies other than th dollar," one observer

By Andrew Cass
INQUIRER STAFF WR
The Mexican bailout,
fiscal year. A waveri
serve. A gridlocked
All were being
for the stomach-i
dollar, a plunge tha
of inflation, recession
squeeze on American liv
ards.
The dollar fell to a record lo
92.59 yen in late afternoon tradi
New York, down from Friday's
93.70. It also declined again
man mark, dropping
marks, th
level
ear

OP-ED DEPT

The letter arrives at the Op-Ed Department.

INCOMING LETTERS

EDITOR

The letter is read by an editor.

Once approved, it goes to the fact checker who verifies the information in the letter.

FACT CHECKER

PROOF READER

The letter then goes back to the Op-Ed Department, where it is edited for publication.

1 Explore Your Options

Think about a list of topics for a letter to the editor. Focus on issues that are important in your school or community, and choose the one you care about the most. Research the topic by reading community newspapers, talking to people, and listening to the local news. Take notes as you do your research. Decide what your opinion is about the issue.

TOOLS

- paper and pen
- local newspapers
- envelope and stamp

VIDEO
Recycling
VHS

Tips
- If you want, work with a classmate to gather information about an issue. You take one side of the issue, and your friend takes the other.
- Interview people and write down their opinions. Be sure to get their names.
- Call or write to community leaders and see how they feel about the issue.

2 Organize Your Information

Once you have researched the issue you want to write about, it's time to outline your letter. The first part of your letter will introduce the issue. The second part will give facts and maybe some quotes about the issue. Your last paragraph will state your opinion on the issue and any suggestions you might have. Make notes about what you will include in each part of your letter.

How Am I Doing?

Before you write your letter to the editor, take a few minutes to ask yourself these questions.

- Did I pick an issue that's important to my community?

- Did I gather facts and examples to support my opinion?

- Did I make an outline to organize my material?

WE RECYCLE

On the right side of a piece of paper, write your address and the date. On the left side, write the newspaper's address. (You can find this information inside the newspaper.) Then write *Dear Editor,* and begin your letter. Use persuasive writing to get your point across, and support your opinions with facts and quotes. End with *Yours truly* or *Sincerely.* Sign your letter in script, and print your name underneath. Use this letter to create a class Op-Ed page. Mail a copy of your letter to the local newspaper, too. Be sure to put a stamp on the envelope!

4 Assemble the Op-Ed Page

Gather all the letters in the class to create a big Op-Ed page. You may wish to use mural paper or a posterboard as the base. Work together to arrange the letters. Make up a name for your class newspaper, and then add the date. Display the Op-Ed page on a school bulletin board so that everyone can read it.

If You Are Using a Computer ...

Write your letter on the computer in the letter format. Choose a letterhead and create your own personal stationery. You also may want to create a headline banner for your Op-Ed page, using a large special font.

THE OPINION BOARD

CONGRATULATIONS
You have learned that it's possible to create change. Remember to use the skills you've learned to help you take a stand on important issues.

Suki Cheong
Editor ▶

Glossary

ab•o•li•tion•ist
(ab ə lish′ə nist) *noun*
A person who worked to abolish slavery. Frederick Douglass was a famous *abolitionist*.

ac•com•plish
(ə kom′plish) *verb*
To complete; achieve.

ac•tiv•ist
(ak′tə vist) *noun*
A person who takes action to help the community.

ap•a•thet•ic
(ap′ə thet′ik) *adjective*
Having little interest; indifferent.

boy•cott
(boi′kot) *noun*
A planned refusal to have anything to do with a person, group, or nation. They organized a *boycott* of imported products.

Word History

Boycott comes from a person's name. In 1897 an English landlord named Charles Boycott refused to lower rents on his property in Ireland. The tenants responded by paying him no rent at all.

---

civ•il rights
(siv′əl rīts) *noun*
The rights of personal liberty guaranteed to U.S. citizens by the Constitution and acts of Congress.

com•mu•ni•ty
(kə myōō′ni tē) *noun*
All the people who live together in one area.

coun•cil meet•ings
(koun′sel mēt′ ings) *noun*
Gatherings of city or county government officials to make laws.
▲ council meeting

---

hos•til•i•ty
(ho stil′i tē) *noun*
Resistance; conflict; ill will. She felt the soldier's *hostility*.

hu•mil•i•a•tions
(hyōō mil′ ē ā′shənz) *noun*
Offensive, insulting acts. The hero suffered many *humiliations* before he reached his goal.
▲ humiliation

Word History

The word **humiliations** comes from the Latin word *humiliatus* which means "to humble."

---

ir•ri•gat•ed

(ir´i gā tid) *verb*
Brought water to dry
land to help crops grow.
We *irrigated* the fields in
the summer. ▲ **irrigate**

irrigated

lob•by•ing

(lob´ē ing) *verb*
Trying to convince
lawmakers to vote a
certain way. They were
lobbying the town coun-
cil to build a park.
▲ **lobby**

log•ging

(lo´ging) *verb*
Cutting trees for lumber.
▲ **log**

logging

march•ing

(mâr´ching) *verb*
Moving forward in a
steady way, in step with
others. ▲ **march**

marching

a	add	o͝o	took	ə =
ā	ace	o͞o	pool	a in *above*
â	care	u	up	e in *sicken*
ä	palm	û	burn	i in *possible*
e	end	y͞oo	fuse	o in *melon*
ē	equal	oi	oil	u in *circus*
i	it	ou	pout	
ī	ice	ng	ring	
o	odd	th	thin	
ō	open	th	this	
ô	order	zh	vision	

meet·ing
(mē′ting) *noun*
A coming together of two or more people for a common purpose.

news·pa·per
(nōōz′pā′pər) *noun*
A printed paper published daily or weekly that contains news.

op·pos·ing
(ə pō′zing) *verb*
Being against something; resisting. The town was *opposing* the construction of a new highway.
▲ **oppose**

op·pressed
(ə prest′) *adjective*
Persecuted; governed unjustly. The people felt *oppressed* by the new laws.

or·gan·i·za·tion
(ôr′gə nə zā′shən) *noun*
A group of people who work together for a particular purpose.

o·ver·come
(ō vər kum′) *verb*
To get the better of someone or something.

pe·ti·tion
(pə tish′ən) *noun*
A formal written request usually signed by those who support it.

plan (plan) *noun*
A method or way of doing something that has been thought out beforehand.

Thesaurus
plan
proposal
project
design

plan·ta·tions
(plan tā′shənz) *noun*
Estates in tropical regions that grow cultivated crops.
▲ **plantation**

pledge (plej) *noun*
A solemn promise. She made a *pledge* to help the workers.

Thesaurus
pledge
promise
oath
guarantee

pol·lut·ed
(pə lōō′tid) *verb*
Poisoned the environment with waste. The factory *polluted* the water with chemicals.
▲ **pollute**

proc·ess (pros′es) *noun*
A series of actions that will achieve a purpose.

Thesaurus

process
method
system
procedure

pro·duc·tion
(prə duk′shən) *noun*
The act of making
something. The company's
methods of *production*
were better this year.

pro·pos·al
(prə pō′zəl) *noun*
A plan that is presented
to others for their
consideration.

raise (rāz) *noun*
An increase in salary.

re·spon·si·ble
(ri spon′sə bəl) *adjective*
In charge of something.
She is *responsible* for
setting up the chairs.

scab (skab) *noun*
A worker who takes the
place of another worker
on strike. The striking
miners hissed at the *scab*.

seg·re·ga·tion
(seg′ri gā′shən) *noun*
The separation of one
group from the rest of
society.

Word History

The word **segregation**
comes from the Latin
word *segregare,* which
means "to flock apart."

stand (stand) *noun*
A firm opinion about an
issue. He took a *stand*
against slavery.

Word Study

The word **stand** can mean:
- to be on your feet;
  not sitting
- to occupy a place or
  location
- the place a witness sits
  to testify in court
- a small open-air place
  where things are sold

strike (strīk) *verb*
To stop work until
certain demands have
been met. The union
decided to *strike*.

**Un·der·ground
Rail·road**
(un′dər ground′ rāl′rōd′)
noun
The name of the escape
system used by slaves in
the South to travel north
to freedom.

Fact File

- From the 1840s to the
  1860s, the **Underground
  Railroad** helped 60,000
  slaves escape to freedom.

- Harriet Tubman, a famous
  "conductor," helped over
  300 slaves escape to
  freedom.

un·ion
(yo͞on yən) *noun*
A group of workers
who join together to
improve their working
conditions and protect
their interests.

zo·ol·o·gist
(zō ol′ə jist) *noun*
A scientist who studies
animals.

a	add	o͞o	took	ə =
ā	ace	o͞o	pool	a in *above*
â	care	u	up	e in *sicken*
ä	palm	û	burn	i in *possible*
e	end	yo͞o	fuse	o in *melon*
ē	equal	oi	oil	u in *circus*
i	it	ou	pout	
ī	ice	ng	ring	
o	odd	th	thin	
ō	open	th	this	
ô	order	zh	vision	

Authors & Illustrators

Natalie Babbitt *pages 32–39*

When Natalie Babbitt was a girl, she spent much of her time drawing and reading fairy tales and myths. Although this author has done a lot of teaching, she doesn't believe that you can teach someone to write. "Nobody can teach you to write a beautiful sentence," she says. "You've got to learn how to do that by reading."

Peter Golenbock *pages 84–97*

This author loves baseball! His two dogs are named after baseball players and his childhood dream was to be a famous baseball player. When Mr. Golenbock was thirteen, he met Jackie Robinson and got to shake his hand. "Mine disappeared in his," he remembers.

Phillip Hoose *pages 62–73*

Phillip Hoose is a lot like James Ale, the boy in his book *It's Our World, Too!* James tries to get a playground built so children will stay out of the busy street. Mr. Hoose also tries to protect people—and animals. At the Nature Conservancy, he works to identify and protect the homes of endangered species. He has also worked to find good living conditions for people in poor inner-city neighborhoods.

Steven Kellogg *pages 32–39*

Award-winning author/illustrator Steven Kellogg has always loved to draw. As a child, he made up stories for his two younger sisters. He would sit between them and scribble pictures on a big pad of paper as he told a story. He does the same thing today! Only now he doesn't scribble, but spends a lot of time on each image. "I'm constantly rethinking, refining, reworking, rearranging," he says.

"Words and pictures are like two voices, singing different melodies. Together, they blend to make it more meaningful than either voice could be on its own."

Faith Ringgold *pages 10–31*

The family traditions of storytelling and sewing inspired Faith Ringgold in creating her unique form of picture books. Her stories are told on "story quilts" that combine sewing, painting, and storytelling on a patchwork quilt. *Dinner at Aunt Connie's House* is based on her "Dinner Quilt," which has been exhibited at major museums throughout the country.

Lannis Temple *pages 112–113*

Lannis Temple was unhappy being a lawyer, so he decided to do what he loved best: travel. Everywhere he went, he met friendly people. And he saw pollution. He decided to gather together letters and drawings from children all over the world who were also concerned about pollution.

Books &

Author/Illustrator Study

More by Faith Ringgold

Tar Beach
Faith Ringgold's first picture book is based on her own childhood memories of warm summer nights in the city.

Aunt Harriet's Underground Railroad in the Sky
This book combines great art, historical facts, and a fantasy adventure to create a portrait of Harriet Tubman. She exemplified the courage of all those who traveled on the Underground Railroad.

Fiction

Jackson Jones and the Puddle of Thorns
by Mary Quattlebaum
illustrated by Melody Rosales
Jackson is hoping to get a new basketball for his birthday. Instead, he gets a plot in a community garden! What does a city boy know about growing flowers?

Oh, Honestly, Angela!
by Nancy K. Robinson
Angela watches as her older sister and brother try to raise money for Rescue the Children. Determined to help out, Angela takes matters into her own hands, with hilarious results.

Nonfiction

Is There a Woman in the House... or Senate?
by Bryna J. Fireside
These ten true stories tell about American women who made their mark in politics.

The Scholastic Encyclopedia of the Presidents and Their Times
This book, full of pictures and facts, gives a history of our presidents.

Wanted Dead or Alive: The True Story of Harriet Tubman
by Ann McGovern
This dramatic biography tells the story of the courageous woman who led many slaves to freedom.

Harriet Tubman

&Media

Videos

And the Children Shall Lead
Public Media Video/ WonderWorks
The year is 1964 and the Civil Rights Movement is just gaining momentum. Twelve-year-old Rachel proves that children can make a difference. (60 minutes)

Brontosaurus
Video Gems
A boy fears that the littered forest near his home will soon become extinct. (70 minutes)

Sadako and the Thousand Paper Cranes
Informed Democracy
Sadako survived the atomic bomb that fell on Hiroshima when she was two, only to develop leukemia at eleven. Her courage inspired an international peace movement. (30 minutes)

Software

Ace Reporter
Mindplay
(Apple, IBM, MAC)
Read teletypes and conduct interviews to gather facts for writing an article.

Instant Survey
MECC
(Apple)
What issues matter to you? Use this program to design and conduct your own surveys on subjects that you find important.

Newsroom
Queue
(Apple, IBM)
Design, produce, and print your own newspaper. A large library of clip art is included to help you illustrate your articles.

Magazines

Scholastic News
Scholastic Inc.
This award-winning publication brings the world to you.

U*S* Kids
Field Publications
This magazine will keep you up-to-date with what is happening all over America.

A Place to Write

Children's Express
30 Cooper Square, 4th floor
New York, NY 10003

Write to this international news service, for and about young people, to find out how you can become a reporter for them.

Acknowledgments

Grateful acknowledgment is made to the following sources for permission to reprint from previously published material. The publisher has made diligent efforts to trace the ownership of all copyrighted material in this volume and believes that all necessary permissions have been secured. If any errors or omissions have inadvertently been made, proper corrections will gladly be made in future editions.

Front cover: Illustration from LEOPARD from HOW THE ANIMALS GOT THEIR COLORS by Michael Rosen. Illustration copyright © 1992, 1991 by John Clementson. Reprinted by permission of Harcourt Brace & Company.

Back cover: Top: Cover by Peter Spacek. Middle: Cover by Dugald Stermer. Bottom: © Mark Selinger/Outline Jennifer Hazen 1986.

Acknowledgments

Grateful acknowledgment is made to the following sources for permission to reprint from previously published material. The publisher has made diligent efforts to trace the ownership of all copyrighted material in this volume and believes that all necessary permissions have been secured. If any errors or omissions have inadvertently been made, proper corrections will gladly be made in future editions.

Unit Opener: Dugald Stermer.

Interior: Selection and cover from THE MOON OF THE ALLIGATORS by Jean Craighead George. Text copyright © 1991 by Jean Craighead George. Illustrations copyright © 1991 by Michael Rothman. Reprinted by permission of HarperCollins Publishers.

"Alligators" and cover from OXFORD CHILDREN'S ENCYCLOPEDIA by Oxford University Press. Copyright © 1991 by Bob and Clara Calhoun. Reprinted by permission of Oxford University Press.

"Ali Baba Hunts for a Bear" and book cover from ALI BABA BERNSTEIN, LOST AND FOUND by Johanna Hurwitz, illustrated by Karen Milone. Text copyright © 1992 by Johanna Hurwitz. Cover illustration © 1992 by Karen Milone. By permission of Morrow Junior Books, a division of William Morrow & Company, Inc.

"Nature log" illustration from NATURE ALL YEAR LONG (p. 43) by Clare Walker Leslie. Copyright © 1991 by Clare Walker Leslie. By permission of Greenwillow Books, a division of William Morrow & Company, Inc.

Selection and cover from SWIMMING WITH SEA LIONS by Ann McGovern. Copyright © 1992 by Ann McGovern. Reprinted by permission of Scholastic Inc.

Selections and cover from THIRTEEN MOONS ON TURTLE'S BACK by Joseph Bruchac and Jonathan London, illustrations by Thomas Locker. Text copyright © 1992 by Joseph Bruchac and Jonathan London, illustrations copyright © 1992 by Thomas Locker, Inc. Reprinted by permission of Philomel Books.

"Leopard" text from FOLK TALES OF LIBERIA, edited by Richard Bundy, U.S. delegation to Liberia. *Journal of American Folklore* 31:121 (1918). Illustrations and cover from HOW THE ANIMALS GOT THEIR COLORS by Michael Rosen, illustrations copyright © 1992, 1991 by John Clementson. Reprinted by permission of Harcourt Brace & Company.

"Twig diagram" from NATURE ALL YEAR LONG (p. 17) by Clare Walker Leslie. Copyright © 1991 by Clare Walker Leslie. By permission of Greenwillow Books, a division of William Morrow & Company, Inc.

"In Your Own Backyard" and cover from THE CITY KID'S FIELD GUIDE by Ethan Herberman. Copyright © 1989 by Ethan Herberman and WGBH Educational Foundation. Reprinted by permission of the publisher, Simon & Schuster Books for Young Readers, New York.

Selection and cover from SECRETS OF A WILDLIFE WATCHER by Jim Arnosky. Copyright © 1983 by Jim Arnosky. Text and illustrations by permission of Lothrop, Lee & Shepard Books, cover by permission of Beech Tree Books, divisions of William Morrow & Company, Inc.

Selection and cover from THE MIDNIGHT FOX by Betsy Byars. Copyright © 1968 by Betsy Byars. Used by permission of Viking Penguin, a division of Penguin Books USA, Inc. Cover illustration used by permission of Scholastic Inc.

Cover from COME BACK, SALMON by Molly Cone, photographs by Sidnee Wheelwright. Photographs copyright © by Sidnee Wheelwright. Published by Sierra Club Books.

Cover from CHARLOTTE'S WEB by E. B. White, illustrated by Garth Williams. Illustration copyright © renewed 1980 by Garth Williams. Published by HarperCollins Publishers.

Cover from LISTENING TO CRICKETS by Candice F. Ransom, illustrated by Shelly O. Haas. Illustration copyright © 1993 by Carolrhoda Books, Inc. Published by Carolrhoda Books, Inc.

Cover from THE SECRET OF THE SEAL by Deborah Davis, illustrated by Judy Labrasca. Illustration copyright © 1989 by Judy Labrasca. Published by Crown Publishers, Inc., a division of Random House, Inc.

Photography and Illustration Credits

Photos: pp. 2-3: Background © Carr Clifton. p. 4 c: © Ana Esperanza Nance for Scholastic Inc.; tc: © Art Wolfe/Tony Stone Images. p. 5 c: © Ana Esperanza Nance for Scholastic Inc.; tc: © Art Wolfe/Tony Stone Images; all others: © Richard Megna/ Fundamental Photographs for Scholastic Inc. p. 6 c: © Dean Siracusa/FPG International Corp.; tc: © Art Wolfe/Tony Stone Images; bc: © Scott Campbell for Scholastic Inc. pp. 22-23 bc: © Tom & Pat Leeson/DRK Photo. p. 24 tl: © Larry Lee for Scholastic Inc.; bl: © Larry Lee for Scholastic Inc.; ml: Larry Lee for Scholastic Inc.; tc: © Bie Bostrom for Scholastic Inc.; tr: © Bie Bostrom for Scholastic Inc. pp. 24-25 br: © Scott Campbell for Scholastic Inc. p. 25 tr: © Ana Esperanza Nance for Scholastic Inc. p. 26 c: © Bie Bostrom for Scholastic Inc.; bl: © Tom Ulrich/Tony Stone Worldwide; tc: © Bie Bostrom for Scholastic Inc.; bc: © Bie Bostrom for Scholastic Inc. pp. 26-27 br: © Geo. F. Godfrey; tr: © John Gerlack/Earth Scenes. p. 27 mr: © Scott Campbell for Scholastic Inc. p. 42 bl: © Tim Davis/Tony Stone Images; cr: © Tony Stone Images/Brian Stablyk; br: © call/Bruce Coleman, Inc. p. 43 br: © Gregory K. Scott. p. 44 c: © John Lei for Scholastic Inc. p. 45 br: © Scott Campbell for Scholastic Inc.; tr: © Comstock Red; bc: © Jim Brandenburg/Minden Pictures; bl: © Ana Esperanza Nance for Scholastic Inc. p. 76 bl: © John Lei for Scholastic Inc.; br: © Scott Campbell for Scholastic Inc. pp. 76-77 c: © John Lei for Scholastic Inc. p. 77 br: © John Lei for Scholastic Inc. p. 78 bl: © 1995, Richard Megna/ Fundamental Photographs; cr: © Hans Reinhard/ Bruce Coleman Inc.; tr: © Richard Lee. p. 79 cl: © Bruce Coleman Inc.; bl: © John Lei for Scholastic Inc. pp. 82-83 © Jack D. Teemer, Jr. p. 84 tl: © Charles Palek/Animals Animals; p. 85 br: © Photo Researchers; bl: © Walter H. Hodge/Peter Arnold. p. 88 tc: © Photo Researchers, Inc. p. 120 tc: © Douglas Faulkner/Photo Researchers, Inc. pp. 120-121 br: © Doug Perrine/DRK Photo. p. 121 tr: © Lee Kuhn/FPG International Corp. p. 122 bc: © Tony Stone Images. p. 123 tr: © Walter Hodge/Peter Arnold, Inc. p. 124 cl: © courtesy of Scholastic Trade Department; bl: © Carol Bruchac. p. 125 tr (Jean Craighead George): courtesy HarperCollins Children's Books; cr (Johanna Hurwitz): © Amanda Smith; br: courtesy of Scholastic Trade Department. p. 126 bc: © Charles Krebs/The Stock Market. p. 127 cr: © Renee Lynn/Tony Stone Images; tl: © Chlaus Lotscher/Peter Arnold, Inc.; br: © Stephen Ogilvy for Scholastic Inc.

Illustrations: pp. 8-9: Anatoly Dverin; pp. 11-12, 15, 18-19, 21: Evangelia Philippidis; pp. 28-35, 37-41: Michele Noiset; pp. 46-47: Anatoly Dverin; pp. 80-81: Anatoly Dverin; pp. 100-101, 103-106, 108-113: Tim Lee.

Acknowledgments

Grateful acknowledgment is made to the following sources for permission to reprint from previously published material. The publisher has made diligent efforts to trace the ownership of all copyrighted material in this volume and believes that all necessary permissions have been secured. If any errors or omissions have inadvertently been made, proper corrections will gladly be made in future editions.

Unit Opener: © Mark Selinger/Outline/Jennifer Hazen 1986.

Interior: "Dinner at Aunt Connie's House" from DINNER AT AUNT CONNIE'S HOUSE by Faith Ringgold. Text and illustrations copyright © 1993 by Faith Ringgold. Reprinted by permission of Hyperion.

"The Last Days of the Giddywit" by Natalie Babbit from THE BIG BOOK FOR OUR PLANET. Text copyright © 1993 by Natalie Babbit. Reprinted by permission of the author. Illustrations copyright © 1993 by Steven Kellogg, first published by E. P. Dutton in THE BIG BOOK FOR OUR PLANET.

"Eye on the Prize" is excerpted from *ZuZu Journal*, September/October 1993. By permission of Restless Youth Press, 271 E. 10th Street, #64, New York, NY 10009. *ZuZu* logo used by permission.

Survey from BRIGHT IDEAS: ENVIRONMENTAL STUDIES by Alistair Ross. Copyright © 1988 Scholastic Publications Ltd. "Families and Free Time" bar graph (p. 47) based on graph from *Scholastic News*, vol. 53, no. 17, February 15, 1985.

Selections and cover from TROUBLE AT THE MINES by Doreen Rappaport. Text copyright © 1987 by Doreen Rappaport. Reprinted by permission of HarperCollins Publishers.

"James Ale" and cover from IT'S OUR WORLD, TOO! by Phillip Hoose. Copyright © 1993 by Phillip Hoose. Reprinted by permission of Little, Brown and Company.

American Red Cross Public Service Announcement used by the kind permission of The American Red Cross.

"Teammates" from TEAMMATES by Peter Golenbock, illustrated by Paul Bacon. Text copyright © 1990 by Golenbock Communications, Inc. Illustrations copyright © 1990 by Paul Bacon. Reprinted by permission of Harcourt Brace and Company.

"Save My Rainforest" from SAVE MY RAINFOREST by Monica Zak, illustrated by Bengt-Arne Runnerström, English version by Nancy Schimmel. Text copyright © 1987 by Monica Zak, English language text copyright © 1992 by Volcano Press, Inc. Originally published in Sweden under the title RÄDDA MIN DJUNGEL by Bokförlaget Opal, 1989. This edition is published by special arrangement with Volcano Press, Inc.

Selections and cover from DEAR WORLD, edited by Lannis Temple. Copyright © 1992 by Lannis Temple. Reprinted by permission of Random House, Inc.

Cover from CLASS PRESIDENT by Johanna Hurwitz, illustrated by John Rosato. Illustration copyright © 1991 by John Rosato. Published by William Morrow & Company, Inc.

Cover from THE GREAT SQUIRREL UPRISING by Dan Elish, illustrated by Denys Cazet. Illustration copyright © 1992 by Denys Cazet. Published by Orchard Books.

Cover from SWEET CLARA AND THE FREEDOM QUILT by Deborah Hopkinson, illustrated by James Ransome. Illustration copyright © 1993 by James Ransome. Published by Alfred A. Knopf, Inc.

Cover from WHERE WAS PATRICK HENRY ON THE 29TH OF MAY? by Jean Fritz, illustrated by Margot Tomes. Illustration copyright © 1975 by Margot Tomes. Published by The Putnam Publishing Group.

Photography and Illustration Credits

Photos: © John Lei for Scholastic Inc., all Tool Box items unless otherwise noted. p. 2 cl: © John Bessler for Scholastic Inc.; bl, tl: © James Lukoski for Scholastic Inc. pp. 2-3 background: © John Lei for Scholastic Inc. p. 3 bc: © James Lukoski for Scholastic Inc.; tc: © Ana Esperanza Nance for Scholastic Inc. pp. 4-6: © Ana Esperanza Nance for Scholastic Inc. pp. 8-9 © Paul Barton/The Stock Market. pp. 40-41 bc: © Henry Garfunkel. pp. 44-45 br: © David S. Waitz for Scholastic Inc. p. 46 bc: © Stanley Bach for Scholastic Inc.; br: © Mike Wilson/FPG Interntional. p. 47 bc: © Stanley Bach for Scholastic Inc.;br:John Lei for Scholastic Inc. pp. 48-49: © The Bettmann Archive. p. 62 bc: © Ana Esperanza Nance for Scholastic Inc. pp. 72-73: © Ana Esperanza Nance for Scholastic Inc. p. 74 cl: © John Lei for Scholastic Inc.; tl, bl: © James Lukoski for Scholastic Inc.; tr: © John Bessler for Scholastic Inc.; tc: © Ana Esperanza Nance for Scholastic Inc. pp. 74-75 c: © John Lei for Scholastic Inc. p. 75 tr: © John Bessler for Scholastic Inc. p. 76 bl: © John Lei for Scholastic Inc.; tr: © John Bessler for Scholastic Inc. p. 77 cr, tr: © John Lei for Scholastic Inc.; bl: © John Bessler for Scholastic Inc. pp. 78-79 bc: © John Lei for Scholastic Inc. p. 80 br: © Stanley Bach for Scholastic Inc.; bl: © John Lei for Scholastic Inc. p. 81 tr: © J. Taposchaner/FPG International. pp. 82-83: © C.C. Lockwood/Earth Scenes. pp. 84-85 tl: © Richard Megna/Fundamental Graphics. pp. 114-115 bc: © John Lei for Scholastic Inc. p. 116 bl, c: © John Lei for Scholastic Inc.; br: © Stanley Bach for Scholastic Inc. p. 117 bl, tl: © John Lei for Scholastic Inc.; br: © Ken Reid/FPG International. tr: © Stanley Bach for Scholastic Inc. p. 118 br: © Joseph Devenney/The Image Bank; bc: © Stanley Bach for Scholastic Inc.; stamps: © John Lei for Scholastic Inc. p. 119 c: © Stanley Bach for Scholastic Inc. p. 121 c: © Robert Reiff/FPG International Corp.; lc: © Errol Andrew/FPG International Corp.; cr: © Larry Grant/FPG International Corp. p. 124 tl: © Avi; cl: © Courtesy of Harcourt Brace; bl: © Little Brown & Company, Boston. p. 125 tr: © Courtesy of Penguin USA; br: © Courtesy of Lannis Temple. p. 126 bl: © Schomburg Center for Research in Black Culture; p. 127 br: © Stephen Ogilvy for Scholastic Inc.

Illustrations: pp. 64, 67, 70: Lyle Miller. pp. 114-115: Jared D. Lee.